D1614384

The Compleat Traction Engineman

E. E. KIMBELL

LONDON
IAN ALLAN LTD

First published 1973

ISBN 0 7110 0437 4

Published by Ian Allan Ltd, Shepperton, Surrey
and printed in the United Kingdom by
A. Wheaton & Co., Exeter

Contents

Foreword

When Esmond Kimbell asked me to contribute a foreword to this book I felt particularly inadequate for the task for in the days when he was driving a set I was but a boy hanging round any threshing that happened to be going on near at hand. Closer acquaintance with the business came later and the chapters that follow are, to me, marvellously evocative of the sights, sounds and smells inseparable from the task of separating the grain from the ear by steam. No little part of the enjoyment is that the view presented is personal and idiosyncratic to a high degree for how would the flat phrases and measured alternatives of an impartial assessment convey what it was like to work with steam, in its latter days, amidst the broad fields of the South Midlands. The acuteness of the author's observations and his sly asides on the habits of his farmer customers are likewise a source of much pleasure in reading the book.

Since arable farming varied enormously over the country, what is true of Northamptonshire and Leicestershire, despite threads of common practice, will not necessarily reflect the experience of men who worked in Kent or Cornwall or Westmorland and because threshing men were such an individual and opinionated lot they will not all subscribe to the author's views on those things which might be thought to be in common. Thus my friend and neighbour Stan Jacques, who threshed, both as servant and master, from his boyhood till threshing ceased swore by the Ruston machine which Mr Kimbell more or less roundly condemns. I am sure that many others will read the book and disagree with some of the author's views but they will find great pleasure and stimulation in doing so. May it be an immense success.

R. A. Whitehead

Preface

Most enginemen became a little vain: the East Anglian because he could drive straight up to a drum, stop, and the belt would go on and run perfectly; but he was so often on level ground. The Midlander thought he knew more about tackling hills, and so he did; but the West Countryman was even better at it, yet could seldom splice a rope, which many a Beds or Cambs steam-ploughman could do in a meal-break. Yet, strong as the latter might be, knocking a single tube out could make him puff and sweat, when a certain little old boilerman, who seldom took his coat off, would have the lot out in but little more time.

I was no exception, and thought I "knew it all" from soon after being lifted up to open my first regulator until I shut one for the last time as a driver, thirty years later.

Joining the Road Locomotive Society soon showed me that my experiences were by no means unique; that designs were not half so rigid as I had supposed; and that I really knew very little indeed. What follows owes much to Chairman T. B. Paisley's, John Boughton's and Allen Martin's photos and the former's collection of engines; past chairman H. L. Drewitt; A. Duke's engine records; W. M. Salmon's portfolios; George Wright's practical experience; and the Rev. R. C. Stebbing's steam plough knowledge and his aid with crossed and open valve rods.

I was an early member of the National Traction Engine Club, having been present when it was first broached, immediately after Arthur Napper's third Traction Engine Race, in 1952, which I took part in with an 8nhp s.c.Marshall, and the club soon converted this dangerous practice into rallies. I am increasingly amazed at the beautiful engines, recreated from heaps of scrap, coming from its more talented members, and delighted that the one-time worry of the Road Locomotive Society on how to preserve engines, has now been so adequately solved. Through the club I am able regularly to hear, see and smell engines, when for long they had only existed in a dream world; again, I have learned, a by no means solitary one.

Truly there was something magic about a traction engine, and if a little opinionated gossip can be forgiven, was not the Fowler BB ploughing engine the handsomest of all? And did not the BB1's generally longer chimney preserve the gracefulness, as this one was rather heavier on its feet? When owners fitted shorter replacement chimneys, did they really look more powerful? And did their missing a few overhanging boughs over the headland compensate for the extra smoke one got? Was a Fowell ugly, and the Foster over-flared copper top in some way a little menacing? But one could really keep on for ever like this. . . .

1 The Marriage of Boiler and Engine

Few mechanical things were better loved than the steam engine. Flashing rods entrapped the eye, revolutions were slow enough to beat time with and there was gentle warmth and a nice oily smell. As a factory engine or marine engine it went at a regular speed, 80 revolutions a minute for the largest up to 120 or so for smaller ones, establishing a rhythm which worked itself into those who looked after it, as a steady beat so often can. The steam boiler which fed it was alongside or in another department.

In its railway engine guise engine and boiler were one unit, almost everyone knew it and despite some lack of rhythm due to varying speeds, for those with eyes to see, there was often poetry, music and awe. The first generation of drivers were dedicated men. With no roomy cab, or even protective weather board at first, questionable track and signalling making for danger, long hours and low pay they kept at it in all weathers. Perhaps it was the sense of adventure, and there were things the imagination could play with too, like the shapes of the tall bell topped chimneys varying from the austere to the smiling, or a devilish grin if flared too much. It could be fun to make these throw out smoke and sparks and kind of shout back at you; or with an ease of regulator quieten their noise down to a whisper. The clanking, the hissing, and the roar when safety valves opened to release surplus energy could become part of a man and add something to his stature, so that often an engineman could be picked out anywhere. And possessiveness came into it too, as each driver had his own engine, or only shared it with one other.

When increases in size and numbers made separate maintenance staffs necessary and a driver could have a different engine every day, impersonality began to creep in, which, despite improved conditions, made the job less pleasurable. And now, with steam gone from the rails, driving can sometimes be a bore, no matter how comfortable it be made.

The less dramatic traction engine—like the locomotive, one unit—nearly always 'belonged' to its driver, whether he owned it or was an employed man. He cleaned, adjusted, oiled and fired it and only handed steering over to his mate when travelling on the road, preferring to drive and steer himself in the farmyard or field; and he thus developed a feeling for it not un-akin to love. And it attracted a close brotherhood too, being less regulation-bound than the railway engine. It was easier for the inquisitive to get onto the footplate and see what was happening. Much of what it lost in size it gained in rhythm. When coupled by belt to drive a threshing machine or dynamo, governors took over the regulating, keeping the speed about 160rpm, easily remembered, as it is not far off a tom-tom's beat, which runs like a thread through so many patterns of activating music.

It was not so difficult for a keen young man to become a mate, or embryo driver. He merely had to hang around long enough. If his father was a driver things were even easier, as he would be expected to have much of the required skills just under his skin, it being well known that drivers seldom left off talking about engines and their queer ways even at home. Even if he was no nearer to it genealogically than a grandson, there would still, perhaps, be some instinct for engines. But the ideal way for a boy to learn was on a portable engine, as then he was already half trained for traction work.

The portable engine was the forerunner of the traction engine and never entirely replaced it. A few were still to be found on farms driving threshing machinery until the time when tractors replaced traction engines there, and those in saw mills lasted until electricity took over, and there were also many on small sawing sites, where moving was rarely required, and of course used wood for fuel. There was the same locomotive type boiler, with firebox one end and smokebox the other with tubes running through the boiler barrel to take the fumes. The cylinder and motion were on top, the former unusually the smokebox end, with its exhaust pipe running along to the chimney base, where its suction aided their flow and the fire's draught. It was more open and accessible than a traction and as it rarely moved—then by horses in shafts fixed on the turntable the smokebox, end—was the better to learn on, the boiler being always in the same position; whereas a traction's position varied according to the level of the ground it was on when stationary, and when moving—well, that was a more advanced procedure.

This engine was generally single cylindered, giving two 'chuffs' per revolution. A few had double cylinders, when they gave four 'chuffs' like a railway engine, their cranks being set at right angles to equalise the power impulses. Fewer still were 'compounds' where the steam from the first cylinder went into the other, larger diametered, to allow for the steam's expansion en route, when again there would be only two 'chuffs' a revolution. The piston rod went in and out of the cylinder in a straight line to a 'crosshead' sliding up and down between parallel bars. The connecting rod 'elbowed' on to this and went along to the crank, which it turned, like a man turning a handle. But where a man can alter his stance to start a crank from rest by pressing down or pulling up on the handle when it is back towards him or right away from him, the engine's crank would be stuck there if it was in one of those places when steam was put on to start it. Then, the crank had to be moved away a little from either of these 'dead centres', in the same direction it had been running by pulling on the large—often 5 ft or more—flywheel. Thus was a habit begun of always looking at the crank before starting. Steam was let in by moving the regulator handle, not too suddenly, lest the heavy driving belt around the flywheel's slightly crowned rim came off. This handle was between brass labelled bars marked 'open' and 'shut' if a push-and-pull one, or in front of a semi-circled one similarly marked, and handled outwards, if of the 'twisting' type. The handle, called the 'regulator' moved the regulator proper, which was inside the steam chest surrounding the cylinder, opening or shutting steam on its way from the boiler to the cylinder by means of a cast iron slide, kept tight up to its face by the steam's pressure. As the revolutions increased the governor would come into action checking the steam flow in the circular passage, between regulator opening and cylinder by a butterfly valve so that 'even' revolutions were roughly achieved, some 120rpm with a portable; a pleasurable momentum. The governor had plenty to do when sawing was the job, as the 'load' was always changing. While the saw was slicing through a piece of wood the exhaust noise would sharpen up—increasing the draught to the fire—and a little steam leak past where piston rod and valve rod went into the cylinder: at the end of the cut would come a relaxing, with a clicking from inside the cylinder and relieving 'chortles' from the chimney.

The valve rod had a shorter stroke than the piston's and controlled a sliding plate inside, with slots in it, passing over similar slots leading into the cylinder. This put steam first one side of the piston, then the other as it went to and fro, and at the same time took in the

exhaust steam through its own slots to apertures at either end of the
stroke which lead to the exhaust pipe. The valve rod was moved by
an eccentric, an out-of-centre disk on the crankshaft, via a collar
which slipped around this. This was not fixed on solid but bolted to
a concentric disk by a ¾in bolt at the extremity of a short semicircular slot. When the engine was required to work in an opposite
direction, like threshing—crossing a driving belt to do this was less
popular—the bolt was loosened and the flywheel turned by hand
until it reached the other end of the slot and then tightened. Then,
of course, starting positions away from dead centres were in the
adjacent places.

Another eccentric, outside the crankshaft's supporting brackets,
worked the boiler feed pump, fixed alongside it. This sucked water
out of a tub below it on its up stroke and returned it on its down
stroke. When water was required in the boiler, a tap on the return
pipe was closed, which caused the water to go along the more resisting course into the boiler, via a non-return valve, usually a brass
ball resting on a seating. The practice was not to close the tap fully,
but only enough to send water into the boiler at the same rate as it
was being used in the form of steam.

A boy would soon get used to adjusting this to the steam requirements, and to follow the same plan of gradualness in firing. Only a
few logs would be thrown through the firehole door at a time and if
the steam pressure rose too much the ashpan door would be closed
for a while to shut off the air going through from underneath the
firebars. Then the exhaust steam would be noticed coming out of
the chimney white and clear; but as soon as the lid was opened
again and hot air started to mix with the exhaust 'chunking' up
from the chimney base, it would stop, unless the day were a cold one.
A fresh firing up caused black or grey smoke in varying quantities,
more hazy with wood, and then pleasant smelling too.

Inside the firehole door the rectangular firebox could easily be
seen, with rows of 2in and sometimes larger holes in the top part,
30 or so; a screwed-in plug in the 'roof' and what looked like large
rivet holes along its sides—and these were at the back too. The holes
were where the tubes went in which were generally beaded over
that end and protruded a little the smokebox end; the plug was
hollow and filled with lead, which would melt so that the fire would
be quenched whenever the water level was allowed to get lower than
the roof; and the 'rivet heads' were the ends of the stays which held
the box to its outer shell.

There was a glass tube with its base a little higher than the firebox top slanting upwards 9in or so to gauge the amount of water in the boiler held between two short pipes coming horizontally from the boiler barrel (the rounded part). Taps on these kept the steam in should the glass break (and usually had to be turned off by the poker then!) and a slotted length of brass in front gave some protection, and a tap underneath was for periodic 'blowing out' to ensure a correct reading when the water had got muddy. On level ground the engine was best worked with the glass about half full, with more in for head-up positions and less for head-down. Too much caused priming, particularly when the steam pressure was low. This was water getting into the cylinder, which caused severe knocking, washed oil off the cylinder walls, and mixed itself with the exhaust steam, indicated by very white smoke (even with the ashpan lid open) and milky streaks running down the chimney and dribbling over the smokebox.

The steam gauge was a clock shaped device with its single hand traversing a semi-circle marked out in pounds-per-square-inch, often going up to 200lb and more with a red mark at anything between 120lb and 150lb to indicate the maximum working pressure, beyond which steam would start to come out noisily from the safety valves on top. It was fixed higher up to get dry steam. The valves of early portables had weights on levers to hold in the steam, later ones had neater spring-loaded ones.

On top of the collars round the eccentrics were small brass cups, each having a diminutive pipe rising up inside. Wool wound round a piece of wire went into this, not too tightly, with the wool's tale-end going down into the cup. When filled nearly to pipe level with oil and a little squirted over the pipe top, the wick would start to siphon oil through to lubricate the bearing surface between the eccentric and its slipping collar. Careful observation and subsequent adjustment could so regulate the feeding rate that not more than two fill-ups a day would be required. A larger oiler with a screwed brass top surmounted the 'big end'—the 'hand' of the connecting rod which had a forked end to take it—made up of two brass bearings with shim adjustment to the extreme one and a wedge adjuster to the other. (A shim was only added after some wear and a little previous wedge tapping.) Loose wicks splattered oil and marked the careless driver—sometimes liberally!

The governors were a pair of croquet-ball sized weights suspended from the top of a foot-long verticle spindle. Their holding bars had others from them joined at the bottom to a sliding collar at the base of the spindle, which was turned via bevel wheels by a belt from the crankshaft. When this went fast enough the weights began to spread out due to the centrifugal force—like a chestnut on a piece of string when twirled—which lifted the collar up the spindle. A short fork from the collar part-turned a rod which went through into the steam chest to lift a valve in the steam passage from the main regulator.

Thus, when the engine began to slow down because of an increase in load from the machine it was driving the governors' speed lessened with it and the 'croquet-balls' dropped enough to push the collar down and turn the spindle to let in more steam; and when, with the extra load ceasing, this caused the revolutions to build up beyond the desired speed the rising weights checked it again.

Some drivers left the regulator wide open so that the governor could have full play; others, more cautious, only partly opened it lest the belt break and the engine 'run away with itself' and cause damage. Here, of course, when there came an extra heavy load, the recovery time to normal running would take longer.

Later governors were the 'Cross arm' which were half the size and went at twice the speed: or double the crankshaft's. These were better looking with a neat triangular casing over where the weight-holding arms crossed at the top and their inside control valve improved. These lessened the recovery time from a check in speed and cut down overspeeding afterwards, making engines with the older type governors seem slow witted, taking time to think, as it were before doing anything about a set-back or an 'overrev'. A still later governor was the Pickering type, American designed and the best ever. Here the governor sat on top of its regulator or equilibrium valve firmly checked an 'overrev' half way through an exhaust beat if need be, and responded to an increase in load in an instant. Pickering governors were smaller, and had three balls half way down spring slats slightly bowed out when at rest, and were surmounted by a brass knob with a small oil hole on it. An internal spring aided the quick recovery and the actuating rod was the stalk itself sliding down between the spring slats' holding collars. These were great steam savers, and popular, because the engine then cost so much less to run.

The four rods entering the steam chest—the pistons, the valves, the regulators and the governors—first passed through a brass collar held in place by two projecting bolts through flanges at their ends. The entrance bores were large enough part way to allow the collar's entrance also as far as a loose slightly bevelled brass washer. To keep steam from blowing out as the rods moved, rings of 'packing' were inserted between collar and washer and the former then tightened on bolts projecting from the steam chest to press them in. The packing was black rope-like material, asbestos based with plenty of black lead in it, which was both heat resisting and lubricating. The collar was called a Gland and the recessed space the Stuffing Box. A newly packed rod would tend to blow steam after a few days, when an additional ring or two would be added and care taken not to tighten the nuts too much; little more than finger tight was about right, when an additional lock-nut would keep the gland from coming loose. (Similar, but screw-in, glands held the water glass to its receivers, cranked over from the holding pipes.)

The piston and slide-valve, hot and under steam pressure, needed thicker lubricating oil than the outside bearings. This went into a pint sized brass container over the slide-valve. When the top was screwed down a plug cock at its base was turned on just enough (by guess work) for it to drip-feed into the valve chamber. Sometimes there was a second one for the cylinder so that extra lubrication could be got in there whenever the ominous knocking of priming began. In theory the drip only acted when the regulator was open, which let steam into the holder to form an emulsion with the oil. But it was a hit-and-miss method, and the later development of a ratchet worked mechanical lubricator actuated from the valve rod caused many a sigh of relief.

A portable gave a learner enough to keep his eye on until keeping steam became second nature, with the water glass always about half full and the steam gauge needle on the 100lb mark—unless the load was consistently heavy, when he would let it swing to another 10lb or so.

Other things would come later, like not opening the ashpan lid fully in cold weather, lest, when pulling hard on a thin fire, too much air came through the bars to cool the tube ends and make them leak. For the same reason the firehole door would never be left open for long nor firing done when the governors were on the drop. Stay heads could also whimper and a sometimes cure for both would be quickly to make-up a large fire so as to expand the metal again. More often, though, leaking tubes needed a session in the firebox next morning, preferably with ashpan off and bars dropped the night before. Here the tube expanders would go in—a ring of tapered roller bearings with a tapered mandrel in the middle, and be wrung round a time or two by a short iron bar passed through a hole at its end. Stay heads would be hammered over more, with someone outside holding a heavy hammer against the other end of the stay.

A year with a portable was an ideal training for traction engine driving in any of its three branches—threshing, steam ploughing and haulage. Even then a period as driver's mate was an advantage, as extra things to learn when threshing were: feeding the drum; setting; manoeuvring over uneven ground, and field work involving spudding-up and roping. With steam ploughing otherwise the earlier stages of being cook-boy and dragman could be missed, but there was so much beyond mere 'portable' knowledge, even to becoming a competent 'spare' driver—the third man who drove an engine at meal times while the foreman went the rounds of relieving the plough or drag, and the other engine. With haulage he would be promoted all the quicker from steersman to an engine of his own if he already knew how to 'keep steam'.

2 Development

What gave birth to the traction engine was a length of sprocket-chain. A Kent farmer, Thomas Aveling, thought it out. He replaced the portable's short axles which protruded from the firebox sides, with a live axle behind the firebox; put a large sprocket on it and a small one on the crankshaft and connected the two by a chain. The engine was previously prepared by having Stephenson's Reversing Gear fitted, developed for railway locomotives a decade earlier. Here an additional eccentric set at 120 degrees from the other had the rod from it idly swinging a suspended twin bar to and fro. In between this was a square die made to slide up and down between the bars—these were known as the 'link'. Forked onto the die was the valve-rod, in line with the first eccentric's rod. When the link was moved up the die kept its place, held by the valve-rod guide, and in the process became parted from the eccentric rod, while the one which was idling began to approach it, so that at the extremity of the link's movement the erstwhile idling rod had taken over the moving of the valve, leaving the other doing the rocking part. The engine then went round the other way. This did the same job as the bolt-slackening, slot-sliding, bolt-tightening which reversed the portable with only one eccentric, but did it quickly by means of a lever connected by bell-crank to the link. The lever, placed conveniently for the driver's hand, moved between guide bars with a slot in the middle and one at either end into which it 'triggered' for stop, forward and reverse.

One imagines the first driver, after Thomas Aveling had shown him, gingerly fingering the lever as a preliminary to pushing the holding bolt through an extension on the crankshaft sprocket, and so making the engine mobile. But first, if the crank was not in the right position for a start forward he would pull the flywheel round until it was. Then a try in reverse would mean another flywheel-tug if the crank had not stopped just right: not easy then, with the engine

17

in-gear. But it might not take him long to see, that with one hand on the regulator and the other on the reversing lever he could make the engine respond, and so the job itself, merely by letting it go round the 'wrong way' for half a stroke with just a little regulator opening, then slamming the lever over and opening up at the same time. Should he fail to catch the crank right the first time it would not matter much if it went over again: a little practice would soon see the engine becoming fully obedient.

Instead of a team, only one horse, to steer the wagon-type turn-table was now needed and this doubtless felt some surprise at the ease of its task—until the driver pulled his reverse lever back! But steering this way was not so good, really; nor were smooth wheels when the ground was wet. So an extension was made from the turn-table with a sort of bicycle-fork holding a single wheel at the end, which could be twisted by a tiller, the steersman sitting in front of the smokebox. Other modifications were a gearing down of the driving sprockets by a pinion in its place which would slide in and out of the bracket-held driven pinion below it, (for in and out of gear), to which the driving sprocket was fastened; the rear wheels were replaced by wider ones with shallow ridges on the surfaces, to grip the ground; and, copying from the railway engine, the driver had a footplate and a small tender behind him with coal on top and a water tank underneath.

Pilot wheel steering proved uncertain because even with angle irons bolted on, the wheel would not keep its course whenever a turntable wheel went into a depression, or pressed against a large stone; also the extension took up room. So it was replaced by a kind of ship's steering wheel supported by a frame fixed to the smokebox. This turned the 'lock' by bevels and rack-and-pinion, was hard indeed to move, but positive and lasted quite a long time. Some makers—Aveling's example being soon followed—still used it after they had changed the cylinder's position from the firebox-end to just behind the chimney, which was the next gradual development. The crankshaft was then nearer the rear wheels, giving a shorter drive and making it easier to be put in and out of gear. The chain was soon replaced by an intermediate pinion and countershaft between the crankshaft and back-axle, an improvement as chains were expensive to make and apt to break.

After a time it was felt that something should be done to improve a system of steering which gave rise to so much bad language, especially shocking to the early Victorians. "Turn a bit to the right", the driver would shout as he was inching the engine forward to get the flywheel in line with the thresher's pulley. "Come and turn the ———— yourself, then", the steersman would sometimes holler back as he vainly pulled with all his might on the wheel's spoke handles, which would sometimes stick until the vital place of correct belt length had been passed, the ground being more often rough than smooth. Also should the unfortunate driver have too much water in the boiler and priming occur at his next jerk forward or back, giving the steersman a neck full of hot water and soot, the air would again be 'blue', and he could even be at some personal risk!

Thus was steering under the driver's direct control evolved, and made easier too. Chain-and-roller was the method, which lasted right through the traction engine era until the first Ackerman's steering began to be seen on steam wagons. (i.e. steering by stub-axles, car-wise.) Here short lengths of bar with adjustments were on either side of the front axle, joined by chains which crossed over each other before taking a few turns round a 3in roller held by a bracket to the front of the firebox. A pinion was at the end, turned by a worm wheel. The spindle of this, bracketed to the firebox wrapper plate, ran diagonally until within reach of the driver, where there was a steering wheel, with a handle on it for rapid turning, as it was very much geared down.

Except for a few special examples the flywheel's position was standardised on the near side (the driver's left) and most were 6 inches to a foot smaller than the portable's, at 4ft 6in, which caused them to run faster when on the belt, 150–160 being the usual governed speed. The gear train began on the opposite side, and a geared engine would go at about 200rpm—with, of course, the governor belt off—to achieve 3mph. As, however, this was slow for travelling and yet too high for manoeuvring in farmyards and tackling hills, a second speed soon followed. This first took the form of a second crankshaft pinion between the flywheel and bearing a little larger for a top gear to give 4mph, with the other reduced in size for 2mph, meshing into spurs on either side of the counter-shaft and usually keeping the drive from counter-shaft to back axle on the far side. This simple method had two disadvantages, one being the flywheel-overhang causing the track to be wider (as this was partly inside the rear wheel); and the other that careless drivers could find themselves with both gears engaged at once: a difficult position sometimes to 'unlock'. So there followed an improved arrangement, with both top and bottom drive-pinions on the offside of the crankshaft, the former being 'cupped' to receive the other inside it when engaged or in neutral, and the counter-shaft pinion being duplicated, high and low pressing together as one. Gear engagements varied from two levers, with an interlocking device preventing both gears being engaged together, to one lever with an interchangeable fulcrum for high or low.

With increased road use it was soon found that engines caused damage to hard surfaces, thus was the already known differential gear first used for a road vehicle, and it had the additional advantage of making the engine easier to steer. Large facing-each-other bevel-pinions, one fixed to the axle and the other to the wheel meshing with smaller bevels inside them, were built into the axle's spur pinion. An 18in long 2½in diameter bright metal bar, or 'pin' was carried which could be passed through a guiding hole to lock the differential when the going was hard, to ensure that both rears gripped at once then and did not leave one wheel stopped and the other slipping round in the mud. Steering was, of course, harder with the pin in and when a turn was made on a hard surface, 'scuffing' occurred as both wheels were going at the same speed, each on a different radius.

As the axle could now move free of its offside wheel, containing the differential, it only remained for the other wheel to be disconnected from its axle fastening to allow a rope-drum to work on it, and the best place for this was in the near-side gap which made room for the flywheel dipping down. The first rope-drums were integral with the outside of the axle's driving block and machined and flanged, the wheel being fastened to this by a pin similar to the differential lock's, but normally in the In position instead of being carried separately. With the wheel scotched for safety and to prevent it running towards the rope when pulling, the pin would be drawn out by the driver's mate, which allowed the 50 yards of wire rope to be wound out by the engine in reverse and then pulled in again by going forward. Guiding rollers were on the bunker side as most roping was done from the rear, but the wire could also be passed under or over the front axle, which was handy for drawing back a threshing machine between two stacks. Later type engines with two counter-shafts, known as fourshafts (the crankshaft and back axle each being a shaft) had free running rope drums, which could be played-out as the engine moved forward and then clipped tight onto the driving block by a sliding key for pulling. Later designed three-shafts could also have a free drum if required.

Although Thomas Aveling paved the way, parallel development

was going on at Leeds. Here John Fowler and his successors (he died in a hunting accident at the early age of 36) in their search for the best method of ploughing by steam made their own contribution to traction engine design. They proved the double engine system to be the most practical, where each had a cable-drum under its boiler and (early engines) 450 yards of steel rope, so that with an engine on opposite sides of a field, an anti-balance plough or a cultivator (also known as a scuffle or a drag) was pulled to and fro between them. After some 'chopping and changing' of designs the cylinder's position was standardised at the chimney end. Fowler's first idea of a differential was the simple one of fixing each wheel to its outside placed driving-block by tightening a slip band on its surface, in the same way an external contracting brake band works. When a tight turn was required on hard ground the inner wheel's band was slackened, leaving all the drive on the outer wheel, after which it was tightened up again. Since a ploughing engine spent most of its time in a field, where it was better that both wheels should always grip, without any dilution from differentials, this method sufficed for many years. Also, these engines had longer boilers to accommodate the rope drum underneath, and their front axles were placed well forward to discourage side slips towards the rope when pulling, which two factors added to there being better leverage between front turntable and back axle than with the ordinary traction engine, making steering with no differentials less difficult. A disadvantage was slipping bands and the breaking of rust and dirt-encased bolts through over-tightening. Thus later, band-differentials were discarded and each wheel double pinned onto a driving-block. On the largely water-bound roads of the day their passage over a 'bendy' road was hardly noticed. Some owners, however, thought it worthwhile to pay the extra to have ordinary differentials fitted.

The first generation of ploughing engines had what was known as 'back-hand' steering. A large steering wheel a little to the rear of the driver's left had its shaft straight down with a spur wheel at the end meshing with a larger one, axle suspended under the tank. There was a small sprocket on the hub, from which a drive-chain ran forward a yard on either side. This joined long rods (on which were adjusters) running under the ashpan and rope-drum, to link-chains from the turntable. The pull was in a straight line, not crossed as with the worm and roller method, because being lower it would then have collected clods of earth and surface vegetation. This necessitated the steering wheel being turned in an opposite direction from the line of travel, which gave no difficulty to those who knew no other way, odd as it appeared to the uninitiated. There was a small brake-drum on the steering shaft with a wheel-worked tightening band to hold it fast so that a set course could be held unhampered by rough ground when moving forward for the next 'pull', or crossing a field after it had been cultivated first-time-over, when there would be large clods on heavy land. Without the steering brake's help a beginner would sometimes be thrown off while gripping too hard: very dangerous when backing. Although worm-and-chain steering, which suffered less from kick-backs, was an early development in steam ploughing too, it was not in general use there until nearly the end of the era. Drivers 'used to' the other did not like to change their ways, and it was also more expensive to make.

As there was a greater distance between crankshaft and back axle, the road gearing had an extra counter-shaft. Thus did the ploughing engine start off with being a fourshaft long before this became the fashion with most other engines.

Also, early on, were two road speeds, but only one pinion at a time was on the crankshaft. The other was over a stub on the running board, a feature on the off-sides of all engines, and going the full length of the boiler on ploughing engines. A change of gear meant a weight-lifting exercise, with one foot on the board and one on the wheel. First the holding pin was removed, then the pinion slipped off and heaved over to the right and down onto the board. Coming back in a reverse movement, the other pinion would be plucked from its stub, up ended and pushed onto the shaft, followed by a turn back to make the first pinion secure. Sometimes one of these pinions would be dropped to the ground, which meant a jump-down, a wipe in the hole to remove adhering dust and earth and a re-squirt with the oil-can after the heave-ho back to the board again. Drivers seldom put on weight until this system was abandoned! High and low pinions were moved by the same fork and lever into the large double speed pinion on the first countershaft (made like the threeshaft's). The small spur on the outside of this meshed with an almost equal sized pinion on the second counter-shaft. The second's spur was on the opposite end of its axle to mesh with the back-axle's pinion. The counter-shaft pinions were castings and their 2 and 3 ft diameters caused them to have resonance, giving a clear bell-like tone when tapped. When in-gear and not pulling too hard they emitted a pleasant tolling sound, muffled, continuous and in harmony, which, although not loud when near, had a remarkable carrying effect, so that a pair of engines on the road could be heard a mile or more away, first one, then the other, then a duet, as bends in the road, and obstructions came and went between them.

There was a bevel behind the flywheel placed to slide in and out of a receiving bevel on a vertical shaft, by a lever similar to the road wheel engagement lever. The flywheel spokes were gracefully bowed back from its hub to make room for the second bevel and at the end of the shaft a pinion engaged with a large one surrounding the top of the rope drum. This type of engagement was known as 'top change'. As it was often difficult to get out of gear when under load without prolonged 'to and fro-ing' with the reversing lever, another type of engagement was soon designed—but again, in little demand until engines with two cylinders (mostly compounds) became popular, where here there was less room for sliding the bevel in and out. The new method was by a dog-clutch on the vertical-shaft, leaving the bevels permanently in-mesh. It was actuated by a long lever slanting down from close to the driver's left hand. The dogs were 'ratchet' shaped, only gripping one way, unless the lever were pressed down to keep it engaged so as to let out a short length of rope under power. When required the dog came out of engagement as soon as the motion moved backwards, and made life easier, but this was in an age when doing things the easy way was more often frowned upon than praised!

With ordinary fourshaft engines (smaller than ploughing engines), which usually took heavier loads on the roads, more frequent gear changes were necessary; consequently a less primitive gear change was introduced, easier because there was no bevel the flywheel side to take up room. A single cylinder engine had room for high and low pinions that side, within the crank case (or enclosure made up of extensions to the firebox wrapper plates, another Aveling idea, where previously the crank was held by brackets). A back plate faced the driver and sometimes a 'spectacle plate' was the other side, where the connecting rod and link rods went through slots. These pinions were spaced so that a doubled high-and-low pinion on the first countershaft could slide between them for either gear, or stay in the middle for neutral. Some slid on splines, others on a squared shaft, and a lever, well over on the offside, controlled the movement and was then pinned into the desired position. On engines with two cranks, as were most compounds, there would only be room for one gear engagement inside, and the other had to be outside the offside bearing, as on a threeshaft. Here there was sometimes a separate lever for each gear and a connection between them to prevent both being engaged together: at others a complicated arrangement of fulcrum-altering involving shifting pegs from one hole to another.

3 Management and Classification

Keeping steam with a traction engine on belt work was little different from managing a portable, except that the rhythm was faster. Feed water was in a tank under the coal bunker behind and under the footplate, ending close to the firebox, with just enough space for the back axle in between. The tank could be kept full by buckets being tipped into a foot-wide hopper at the back, known as the 'pocket'. Sometimes this was at the side, with its lid forming a step to the footplate. Usually, however, the tank was filled by suction from an adjacent cart, or nearby stream. Steam taken from the top of the boiler was piped to the tank, which it entered through a nozzle. This created a vacuum near it, where a 2in wire-bound hose was fitted by a clip or a screw, and its other end, with a 'rose' on it—a bulbous cast-iron piece with holes—put into the water supply. There had to be no air leaks either at the point of suction or in the pipe or its connection: if the former the pipe had to go into the water further while leaks on the way could be stopped with pads of mud over any 'pin holes'. Air leaking in would snort and gurgle and only when this was stopped was the water going cold into the tank, as less steam then being required for suction. Hot water in the tank made getting it into the water difficult.

When an injector was fitted as well as a pump it was generally confined to road use, because then varying amounts of water went into the boiler, according to how hilly the journey was. An injector also caused a vacuum, but in a brass or gunmetal casing containing cones. The steam supply passing through the cones emulsified the water it sucked in with it and sent it along a pipe leading into the boiler side. Injectors fitted after manufacture often had their delivery on the side of the firebox, where the surface was flat and there was no lagging to disturb: a practice makers were apt to frown on as liable to harm the firebox plate opposite the intake, because of lower temperatures. Users' experience found little to support this view.

A $\frac{3}{4}$in injector worked best a little lower than blowing-off pressure, down to about 75lb per sq in and was the usual traction engine size. Sometimes careful juggling was required with the steam tap and the elongated control to the plug tap at the bottom of the tank, the best place for an injector was at the bottom of the tank, as there was less risk of it sucking in the air, then before steam or hot water ceased to blow out of the hole at its base, and a cheerful singing note began. Then, a gentle increase in the glass's level would confirm that all was going well. Coal particles or grit from the tank would be liable to make it stop, midst protesting clouds of steam. Some road engines and steam rollers had a second $\frac{1}{2}$in injector instead of a pump, which would work down to lower pressures and could be left on longer. This was because pumps did not like speeds much higher than 200 or so rpm, when water would squirt out around the plunger, no matter how carefully packed its gland was. An alternative to a second injector was a geared-down pump, usually three-to-one, which was less trouble and more reliable. Most ploughing engines had two injectors, the larger of these the less sensitive 1in size.

The governor belt ran direct from a pulley-surfaced part of the crankshaft towards the near side and in between the road pinions on a fourshaft single. It was removed when not on belt work and the revs then controlled by the regulator, when up to 350 or so were deemed safe enough. Beyond this there could be a tendency to prime, especially when pulling hard and lowering the steam pressure. It was not usual for ploughing engines to have governors; when fitted they could, of course, drive a threshing machine or saw bench with ease, but they were large and clumsy for the purpose.

Rear wheel diameters varied from 5ft to 8ft and widths from 14in to 20in. Ploughing engines had the widest wheels to spread their load better. Slats, angled to minimise vibration were on the wheel surfaces, $2\frac{1}{2}$ to 3in wide. Most makers had them sloping in such a way that the arrow shaped mark they left on the road pointed away from the line of travel, which was sloping upwards when viewed from behind. When slats did not provide sufficient grip, spuds (cleats or paddles) were fitted. Two or three were sometimes enough to get an engine out of a soft place, but where the going was constantly difficult they were fitted at 18in intervals. Spuds were hooked over the outside rim and securing by a $1\frac{1}{4}$in pin through the $1\frac{3}{8}$in holes there for them. Other holes were spaced in between these and staggered, so that pins with domed heads known as frost bolts could be used as an alternative when crossing a frozen field or on an unmetalled road. Putting spuds on was heavy work and taking them off was worse. Sometimes the cottars holding the pins would block fast with hard mud and have to be cut out with a cold chisel. This was not easy from the inside of a wheel; cottars inserted on the outside soon distorted with their contact with the ground.

Fourshaft engines had a metal box in between the front wheels, some round and some square where the spuds and their bolts and cottars were kept; threeshaft engines usually had bars along the offside of the boiler to hang them on and a box under the running board there for the bolts. The reason for this difference is obscure. Some makes had a bar from the centre of the front axle to a bracket on the front of the firebox just under the steering roller, while others did without this, with no apparent harm being done. A time could come, however, with a smokebox being allowed to get too thin, and sometimes holes coming in the base due to burning, and acids from ash. Then a front axle with no lateral strengthening could move dangerously back should the front wheels strike a rough place together. The bar also took the load off the smokebox when pulling or pushing from the front was done.

Engines were classified into 'nominal' horsepowers, which were an indication of cylinder sizes and had little direct bearing on power output, which varied with steam pressure and rpm. Threshing engines were in 5, 6, 7, and 8nhp sizes. Road engines went up to 10nhp, while ploughing engines began at 8 (although there were a few early 'sixes') and went up to 20nhp with a few export ones larger still. The nhp classification for these was vague. Fowlers preferred their classifications to be in letters like Ks, BBs, BB 1s, and AAs even if owners and drivers persisted in calling them 14s, 16s and, 18s; and these too varied in cylinder bores due to different requirements and fuels, although they might look alike in strokes and boiler dimensions. Fowlers also varied their gear ratios to the vertical shaft, yet never seemed to relate this to the cylinder bore. Taking the two extremes of a large bore with a high ratio to the rope drum and a small bore with a low gear and consequently higher revs, there must have been an optimum. Modern engineering trends would be more in favour of the latter, as giving better torque and little noticeable greater wear of moving parts. This would have met with less agreement earlier on. Their lettering seemed wise when one noticed that the bore and stroke of what was known as the '8nhp Road Loco' was the same as the '16 nhp' ploughing engine, although, of course, the latter's boiler was larger.

A 6nhp single cylindered threshing engine usually had a 10in stroke and 8in bore and developed some 25 brake horsepower at governed revs of 160pm with 100lb per sq in boiler pressure, which was all that was required for threshing a light crop like barley. On heavier going the engine would be worked up to 130lb or more—some had 140lb maximum and others 150lb. A 7nhp had a 12in stroke and 8½in bore; and an 8nhp also a 12in stroke but with ½in increase in its bore, and often a slightly larger flywheel, and so ran slower on the belt and thus developed little more horsepower and consumed but little more fuel, partly offset, however, by the larger grate area, as boiler sizes were proportionately increased. The wheels of sixes and sevens were usually 6ft diameter and 16in wide, with some sevens 18in wide; Eights had 6ft 3in—6in diameters and 18in widths.

The larger the engine the lower the steam pressure needed on belt work and the easier it was to manage then. A good firing up, with the pump adjusted to keep the water level in the glass constant, and it could be left alone for half an hour and more. This was useful when the threshing team was not infrequently a man short and the driver encouraged to take off sacks as well as look after his machinery. An 'Eight' was also better on the road because things were easier for it; but it sank-in more on soft ground; required more room to manoeuvre in—a drawback in a congested farmyard—and used that little more coal: or looked as if it did; much the same thing, as the farmer had to supply the coal to a visiting engine.

A 'Six' suffered from none of the 'Eight's' disadvantages but was inclined to be underpowered and prone to bark away at its work when others would express themselves in a quieter manner. The sharper exhaust would pull the fire through smoke box and chimney at a greater rate and cause wear through burned plates. Hence the 'in between' Seven was the most popular single cylindered threshing engine: a compound, here, was generally a Six as this was about the same weight and power as a single Seven.

Regulators were of the push-and-pull type, placed horizontally or vertically, i.e. sticking up, on top of the back plate. Some pushed to start, others pulled, and some horizontals did both, with a double handle and fulcrum in the middle. Other variants were an upturning to a horizontal handle's end; and Fowler's downward sloping ones sometimes at 5 o'clock sometimes at 7 o'clock.

The reversing lever's 'quadrant' had three notches towards its extremes, and one in the centre. It was the practice to put it in the middle of the three on belt-work. This lessened the travel distance of the valve-rod, because the link, being lifted a little, took on a lever action with the idling eccentric-rod-joint as fulcrum and the top dissipating some of the eccentric's throw. This made for greater economy and the exhaust was softer, because some expansive power of the steam was being used. If the lever was pulled back one more, greater expansion still was provided for, but greater throttling of the exhaust as well, and the motion became jerky, with no further increase in economy. Other reversing gears, such as Walchaerts and its variations, permitted greater use to be made of expansion without hampering the exhaust. These, however, were mostly confined to railway locomotives.

With one exception, which will be mentioned later, English traction engine designers used the compound system, when they wished to take full advantage of expansion, and this meant a second cylinder, larger in diameter, for the expanded steam, and also a higher pressured boiler—as the greater the pressure the greater the expansion. The second cylinder usually had a separate set of motion, and generally there were balance weights on the cranks then. Thus the engine ran smoother than a single, and had greater power and economy.

Compounds were mostly used where the work was harder for longer periods, such as hauling and steam ploughing; indeed, most ploughing engines in the last quarter of their vogue were compounds. Compounds were less popular for threshing, as there was less continuous hard work, and any extra economy was not deemed to balance the extra capital cost. And as threshing was a dusty job, necessitating frequent cleaning of the moving parts, a busy driver seldom liked having two sets of motion to clean, or having to push the long-handled brush through its tubes more frequently, because of the softer exhaust allowing them to become sooty.

On a single cylindered engine the reversing lever was much in use. For a quick stop, after shutting the regulator, it would be pulled to the centre notch, or even beyond, momentarily. If left reversed there would be the beginnings of a reverse movement, which could be taken advantage of if necessary by a little opening of the regulator should a reverse direction be required. When going down hill it would be used as a brake, gradually centred or pulled back beyond if the gradient increased, or if an emergency stop was required; here sometimes helped by a little steam. It would be noticed that with the lever in the reverse when going down hill the pressure indicated on the gauge would begin to rise. This was because the cylinder was then acting as an air compressor, drawing its supply inwards through the exhaust pipe. Often the cylinder taps, (at the extremities of each stroke) would be opened then, to release the air and prevent burning off the piston-rod-packing, as under this sort of pressure and without the lubricating advantage of steam behind it, the packing's sealing powers could be damaged. Care had to be shown when this was done, as the 'psst, psst, psst', would soon make a passing horse shy, and sometimes bolt. The main purpose of these taps, opened together by a rod from the driver's end, was to blow out condensation in the mornings, or after a long stop, although here it was good practice to leave an engine 'on-stroke' with the taps open, so that any steam leaking through the shut regulator did not fill the cylinder and cause leaking packing on piston and valve rods. But some drivers held that the lever was best left in the 'safety position'; the centre notch, thus preventing movement should the regulator be inadvertently opened.

A compound engine's reversing lever was less used. Notching-up was not the practice as the low-pressure cylinder 'looked after' the expansion. With the double braking power of two cylinders, holding down hill required only a small backwards movement. And the cranks were generally 'on-stroke'. If 'off' on the first one—there were only two very small arcs in a revolution when the second one would not be 'on'—a small knob along-side the regulator would be pressed to let a little 'live steam' direct into the low pressure cylinder, to turn one crank enough to bring the other into the right position. It mattered little really if the knob turned it over once or twice when wishing to start on one direction as the regulator could always 'catch up'. Thus manoeuvring with a compound was easier.

The correct stance, when an engine was in gear was to have one hand on the regulator and one on the reversing lever, ignoring the steering wheel until the crank was turning, the odd few feet of ground movement not mattering so much. Next the reversing lever hand came onto the regulator and the regulator hand onto the steering wheel. This could be done with a slight swing of the body. When shunting about over uneven ground it was good practice at 100 revs or less, to regulate in such a manoeuvre to allow the regulator hand to join the other on the steering wheel, as this would then often be jerky and stiff. At slow engine speed, a quick reverse could be made without touching the regulator, and if a long backward movement a right-about-footplate-turn was best when the steering wheel came behind and the non-steering hand could be on the reverse lever for a quick stop or change of direction. An amateur was often picked out by starting, or trying to start, with one hand on the steering wheel, as if it were a car's, with its quick motion. And the amateur going backwards would invariably be facing forwards and frequently turning to look over his shoulder. Many a young driver has been brought to order in the shortest terms for these faults.

4 An Approach to Threshing

A first journey on the road with an unsprung engine, a 5-ton thresher and a 2-ton elevator behind and sometimes a chaff-cutter too, was an experience which shattered the ears and quivered the cheeks. Later, ear-drums would toughen and bended knees or raised heels relieve the shaking. In spite of their angle, the wheel slats caused sympathetic vibrations wherever there were loose parts. The revolutions, no longer under governor control would vary with ground conditions, the driver only adjusting his regulator on a perceptible gradient. The track, angled white scars with the trailers' wheel marks going through them, would last a day or two on a hard road, if the tar was soft.

Sometimes the regulator rod from driver to steam chest would whip and tremble; next the loose and dangling governor weights, no longer stiffened by centrifugal force, would shudder and flap; and every time the drum (as the thresher was called) pushed forward on a slope, freeing the drawbar coupling-pin in its hole where it had been tight with pulling, this would jingle and clatter, and joining the chorus were the spuds in their metal box. At times the steering wheel would vibrate fit to shake the steerman's hand off, as if to warn him not to grip too hard: engines responded better to those who acquired a light touch.

Nine turns of the wheel was the average needed to wind the turntable from one extremity to the other, with between one and two turns to change direction. This play was necessary on rough ground, as the turntable would jerk in its arc and swing vertically over lifts and dips. The steering chains were best tightened for a road journey of any length and a quick way was to slip a few $\frac{1}{4}$ bolts or thick nails between the links.

On a metalled road no force was required to steer, and a hand resting on the rim, providing it was a knowledgeable hand, could keep wheel marks from wandering. The best way to steer was by the chimney, as this was a marker which only moved from a straight course slowly, and eventually one learned to hold the wheel where the chimney centred in its occasional left-and-right wanderings. Quick glances at the front wheel as it aimed this way and that with the turntable's swinging 'in the steering gap' were apt to cause frantic wheel winding in a vain attempt to make corrections too soon. Then the driver, not liking a weaving track behind him, would sometimes give a steering lesson, with a hand which rarely moved, except on a corner, when there was a once-or-twice-over pause, and a slow back-turning correction. As the driver had plenty to do, the quicker his mate learned to steer the better.

Another mate's job was to get down and 'block-up' for a stop, particularly important when changing gear, lest the engine run back (or forward) when the sliding pinions were moved out of mesh and before they could remesh with the new gear, as sometimes, the gears would not 'fit' without a small turn of the crankshaft; often, too, the tapered block had to take the weight before a gear could be disengaged.

A stop for water meant blocking-up also, before removing the lifter-pipe from where it was coiled on bunker or footboard side. One end would be clamped to the suction point, or screwed on with a free-running large lugged nut, receiving a final tap with a spare coupling pin, while the other with its rose—go into the stream—ponds were avoided, as non-running and often polluted water caused priming. If there was mud there the firing shovel would go underneath for protection. A thick washer went between the pipe fastening and suction point. This was kept in the tank pocket where thick wire gauze held it away from the water. The pocket lid had a habit of jolting the rattling chorus at certain road speeds, as the indented mark on its inner surface showed.

While water was being drawn the driver would check the oilers on the crankshaft, and have a look at the fire. Maybe a clinker or two had to be removed with the long handled shovel (which caused such a cacophony wherever it hung or lodged on the engine that it was sometimes kept in the drum and, of course, carefully slaked then after use lest it cause a fire). The fire would then be levelled with the L shaped poker and not disturbed too much as this would blacken it and risk tube leaking. The poker would afterwards be hung down between the spokes of the brake wheel—the brake was rarely used. This wheel-screw tightened an external-contracting wooden-blocked band which embraced a rim extension to the rope drum—in form, not unlike the ploughing engine's 'differential'. Occasionally, if the hill was steep and long the poker would be removed and a few fairly ineffective turns of the wheel given: but back-axle brakes seldom did more than aid reversing-lever braking so that the lever was less in the drawn-back-beyond-the-centre position, as then air would be sucked back through the exhaust pipe and some smokebox-ash with it. Some engines had a bar turned up at one end instead of a wheel which was easier to hang the poker on. Others had their brake on a counter shaft: a more effective place but a dangerous one should the rope-drum fastening pin come out, as there was then no check on 'free-wheeling'. The best type of brake, but seemingly confined to road engines, had a block on the inside of each rear wheel, where the leverage was good and made holding-by-the-reverse unnecessary and saved some burning of packing thereby. (Blue smoke would come from piston-rod-packing towards the end of a long hill after much reverse-holding.) An extra brake was sometimes fitted on the fly-wheel, in the front—out of the belt's way—but not popular as in unthinking hands it could make the rim hot and expand, where there would be a risk, even if theoretical, of the flywheel bursting.

With the shovel back from the stream, the driver would do some firing while the mate coiled and strapped the pipe. Then, if the ground was level and the high gear in mesh, a sharp regulator pull would be given to get the crank over the first time, then closed a little after momentum had been achieved. There was often a front-lifting jerk at such a start, with a noisy snatch behind from the drum's coupling and an echoing from the elevator's with the chimney giving off a hearty first few chuffs, sometimes with a mist of sooty con-densate.

When going down a hill there had to be enough water in the boiler to cover the firebox top or the plug might begin to leak. It was enough just to see it in the bottom of the glass or bobbing up with an extra pull-back of the reverse lever, but as well not to stop when 'bobbing'. If this could not be avoided a front wheel turned into a higher road border could be a little help.

Should a steep up-grade follow there might well be too much water in the boiler, with the glass full beyond the seeing point, and a tell-tale dribbling from the regulator gland. Then was the time to handle the regulator gently, otherwise water would be lifted into the cylinder and priming begin. When the dribbling stopped, how-ever, no harm would be done to open-up with aplomb and 'make her talk'. A good clear-out of tubes and smokebox then resulted, not always appreciated by surrounding countryside within chimney range.

If a spark-catcher* was then 'worn' it would sometimes lift with every chuff. Some drivers held that this attachment was not necessary if the smokebox was swept clear of ash and soot before every journey, and that there was also a risk of it being chuffed right off and falling on someone's head. There is no record, however, of this having happened. They were certainly not a popular thing, the wire-mesh tending to bung up with soot on belt work when there was no vibration. Latterly they become a legal obligation and the police were ordered to investigate an engine without one to ensure that if not seen on top there was one of the type which hung down inside. Of course, the answer to this by a driver without one at all was to start firing up as soon as he thought a policeman was going to stop him, when few wanted to look upwards through an opened smokebox door!

Some engines had sliding firehole doors which would 'chink' in time with laboured exhaust beats when going up a hill, and could glow a dull red on a long one. Swing-open doors having inside baffles, did not suffer from this, and lasted longer.

Knowing the road was a great advantage. The injector could then be started before the top of a hill was reached—rather against the rule but of little harm if timed right—and the regulator eased. This would ensure enough in the glass for the next dip and sometimes avoid a stop at the top for the injector to catch up, or of risking it on the down-grade; and it was here when firing-up was better done so as to save the tube-plate from an in-draught of cold air. The handle which adjusted the ash-pan lid did not warrant neglect on a road journey. Wide open was only for going on the level and when the pressure needed building up. With plenty of blast drawing the air through on a hill, only the smallest opening was advisable; and whenever blowing-off was near the lid was better shut. Traction engine fireboxes were susceptible to changes of temperature, not having a brick arch inside to shield the tube-plate, as did the railway locomotive.

Knowing the farmyard approaches was helpful too. The easiest were those set well back so the tackle could turn in straight off the road. An entrance close to the road meant uncoupling the elevator a yard before the drum's rear axle was in line with the first gate post. The drum was uncoupled and the engine moved forward a

* A bulbous or cylindrical wire 'cage'

length, with the steering wheel being turned outwards. Next the engine was backed away from the gate until across the road at right angles, facing the gate. To bring the lock round in line, then, without the hard work of winding the other way, a wedge could be dropped in front of the leading front wheel and the engine then pressed against it, which would result in the steering wheel spinning round on its own and the lock coming round smartly, with the driver's hand exerting a little braking power by pressing behind the wheel—carefully, here, as he could get a nasty blow from the wheel's handle! An ease-off the wedge for the mate to kick it aside and the engine would soon be halfway through the gateway.

Next the two-hooks (or short chain) were unhooked from the back of the bunker and connected as it turned to pull the drum drawbar round into line, for backing on and recoupling again. The fairly light straw elevator could then be pushed or 'barred' forward to the drum's previous position, the arranged gap by the first uncoupling preventing the drum's rears fouling the elevator drawbar 'stunt and lock'. This would then be full locked round to the drum's coupling point. All was then slowly moved forward with the mate walking behind and the driver often glancing back. Should it be seen that an elevator's back wheel was aiming for the gatepost, an engine-spud, kept behind for the purpose, would be angled in front of each rear wheel, when the whole elevator rear would slide over to miss it. But should there be more bends to come, the elevator would be left on the road and its drawbar replaced by horse shafts carried underneath, for a farmer's man to follow along with it. When corn stacks were in a field near the road the elevator was better horse drawn-in first and the drum push-poled in, the engine at the rear and the mate steering by tugging at the drawbar, prevented from turning too short in the lock by guide chains. If there was no one to help him, resort would be made to lock-wedging, as on the engine front wheels, and the chains adjusted to hold it in any lock. The idea of poling-in was to keep the engine on the hard ground as much as possible. The further into a field, the softer it became, especially if residue from a previous thresh, like scattered chaff and short-straw (cavings), was there.

When the drum was within a yard of its position, there would be a pause to check the levels and if necessary run the low side up on tapering blocks and let the high side drop into a shallow trench, until the spirit-level bubbles on the sides and back were showing. A lever-lifting-device would pull bars coupled closely together on the low side to finish off the levelling, while on the other side those were merely tightened. A drum's main frame had to be still to prevent the sieves' movements being lessened as otherwise they rocked the wheels to and fro. The straw shakers turned at 180rpm and the 'shoes', which held the riddles, at 200rpm. The latter's oscillation was increased when the shakers caught up with them, when the urge for the whole machine to go to and fro would not be resisted for a few moments no matter how tight the wheel chocks.

The 60ft × 6in main drive belt was kept rolled up on the caving riddle—the long one which collected short straws from underneath the shakers and the mate would pull this out putting an end over the $7\frac{1}{2}$in drum pulley and unroll towards the engine, which by now, would be lining up with its chimney facing the back-end of the drum. This is where handling skill came in. If the driver could let go of his regulator and leave the crank just turning over, despite the temptation to keep adjusting it according to the state of the ground, both his hands could be on the steering wheel and on a left-hand steering engine his position would be behind the flywheel. With a right-hand lean over and a glance now and then had to suffice. The pulley could be ignored, as it could give false sighting. Better was it to concentrate on the side of the drum and keep the inside of the flywheel just off it, but in line. Great exactitude was not required as the flywheel and drum pulley had cambered faces. Thus the belt clung to them without difficulty and still did its job even at six inches or so out of line. Of course it was preferable to achieve a straight-in-line set, but when the ground was wet and uneven, the engine's front lock did not always obey the steering wheel, so that near enough was better than wasting time and cutting ruts.

The mate would nod for the driver to stop when the pulled-out belt was level with the engine's rear hub, and if then in line, push the end over the flywheel hub. The driver, standing on the road wheel, would then lift the top of the belt to the top of the flywheel, hold it on and start to turn it, with the mate pushing the spokes upwards from his ground position. The cylinder taps would be open to prevent any steam 'inside' giving unwelcome aid, and the lever be forward (or, on a threeshaft, backward, as its flywheels went in an opposite direction for forward). In half a turn the belt would snap home on the base of the wheel. An over-tight fit would require a strap to hold the top of the belt on as it came round, which was kept looped in the brake wheel for the purpose. Too loose a belt would need to be tightened with the ratchet jack, which was leaned against the front of the wheel with its end in a spud bolt. This would also keep the engine steady when it settled down to the belt work.

A practised driver on level ground seldom needed the mates belt-measuring to tell him his distance. And he would also have a good idea of how much further away he should be for a head-down position or nearer for a head-up one. And the top of the wheel was what counted on a side tipped position; the ₁belt would run, seemingly just as well: but always the drum had to be level. A driver who had served a mate's apprenticeship seldom had difficulty in setting to and handling the drum. It was the non-threshing drivers who had trouble, no matter how expert they were at steam plough-ing or timer hauling. Too much time taken by these in setting was often irritating to a farmer who had men waiting for the threshing to start.

Unless the ground was dry, the rope was always better used to get away from a field entrance site. The engine first backed a length with its rope drum unlatched and the rope end hooked to the back of the thresher (or drum), and paying out (i.e. if it was a fourshaft).* Then it was relatched, scotched and the heavy drive pin withdrawn enough to free the road wheel from its axle fixing, inside the rope-drum. A little steam would be put on in forward gear and the drum would then begin to close the gap, with its lock turned by scotch, and the guide chains loose. Then the engine would go back further aiming a little to the side where the drum front had begun to come over, and the rope then taken alongside to an eye on the turntable at the front end, to pull this further round, when the drawbar would be put on, the rope transferred to this, and the drum then came right round it in a half circle. The rope next went underneath it to the elevator's drawbar, where the turntable was always 'this way', and while this was being slowly pulled back to couple behind the drum, eager hands would be lowering it, removing the linking pins and winding up again to fold over. Some elevators were telescopic, but their handling was similar.

When pulling back over soft ground from between a pair of finished stacks to two more, the rope would be used again. Then it would draw the drum towards it, with the rope hooked first to one side of the chassis and then to the other if there was deviation from the straight, this counteracted side-slewing: the lock-steering chains had to be at their tightest. When belt length was reached the ratchet jack would complete the slewing if need be until lined up. It was not

* A threeshaft engine had to wind-out by power.

a good idea then to try and set the engine to the drum, as one would on hard ground with steering room, because of the risk of cutting ruts which would act like 'railway lines' keeping the turntable in them, no matter how one worked at the steering wheel.

5 Threshing

A day's threshing began by driver and mate arriving at 6.30am usually by push-bike. Drum and engine would be sheeted down but the chimney lid, put on the night before, would be off and if the smoke was not thick yellow but a hazy black, there would be a good fire burning thanks to the farm's horse-keeper (or wagoner), who arrived at 6am. He would also have lifted the ashpan lid.

The driver would first unfurl the back of his sheet and roll it clear from where he stood. Removing the poker from the brake-wheel, he would get this well down on the bars and push along until he reached the tube-plate. He would go over the whole firebox like this. Then there would soon be bubbles from the regulator gland and a cheerful kettle-like singing. Next he would take off the sheet, to be rolled at leisure, and oil the points that were to be used that day—often missing the road gear out. If the mate was still struggling with the larger drum sheet, he would also oil the thresher's four riddle-crank bearings, the bottom shaft of the corn elevator, the corn screen shaft and the straw elevator's bottom shaft and gearing. The mate oiled the top of the corn elevator and the pair of crankshafts holding the four shakers, which meant opening a trap door and crawling along inside. All the other bearings were generally ring oilers requiring weekly attention only. Threshers fitted with ball bearings only became popular later on, when those who went with them were regarded as pampered.

By 7am, the main belt would be on and the engine ticking over with at least 70lb of steam on the clock and the taps open for a spell to clear the condensate. Then a general increase in speed would be made until the drum itself, made up of eight 4ft 6in serrated beater bars—began to hum, the note rising as it reached its full speed of 1,100rpm, and the increasing draw of the exhaust would soon build this pressure up to 100, where it was generally kept.

The driver would then walk round the tackle checking to see that

every belt was driving its pulley. The shaker belt ran off the main
drum spindle, was crossed, to a 3ft pulley on the shaker crankshaft at
the straw delivery end, and from here a 3in pulley drove the straw
elevator with a 2in belt, buckled for frequent adjustments in length,
according to whether the elevator was straight or angled. If it was
angled, small pulleys on angle-irons guided it around the corner.
The riddle crankshaft, bottom winnowing fan or blower, and awner
drives also came off the main shaft. From the awner (or corn cleaner)
a short belt ran to the top dresser fan, above the sackman's head, and
from the riddle-crankshaft there was a drive to the corn screen on
the near side corn elevator, on the other. Both of these were slow
movers, the fans and awners were at near-drum speed.

A belt slipping or coming off could delay material inside and soon
cause a blockage. So the driver's eyes and ears were always on the
alert. He knew well the rhythm of every belt fastener as it clinked
over its pulley and any change in the orchestra soon had him at the
trouble spot.

The mate's job was on top, feeding. Standing in a hole with his
back to the engine he would adjust the safety cover on its ratchet
which guarded the beaters, and receive sheaves of barley or oats,
butts first, from the band-cutter. These he would open out so that
each was properly thrashed and as he acquired the knack an even
flow would result, preventing the engine governors from lowering-
and-lifting and keeping its exhaust beats even.

The band cutter also liked to have his sheaves butts first. These he
would pick up with the flat of his curved serrated knife, and where-
ever a knot appeared on top, would cut next to it and pull out the
string with his other hand. String with knots in the middle collected
straws, and so were rarely saved.

There would be two and sometimes three men on the stack with
long two-pronged pitchforks, one pulling out sheaves and throwing
them to his mate who passed them, butts first by a neat flick of wrist,
to the band cutter. It was mostly 'lifting up' here as the stack increased in density as it lowered. Two, generally older hands, would
be on the straw rick. This was lighter work, but needed skill and
experience if a properly shaped rick was to be achieved.

Two men would be on the ground. A strong one, generally the
wagoner, on the sacks, which weighed 2¼cwt if wheat. After being
unhooked from the drum, sacks would be 'knee hotched',* onto a
lifter and wound up so he could get his back underneath and dump

* hotched by digging knees into the middle and embracing the top.

it into a waiting cart. The second man would be on chaff-and-cavings, the chaff taken in a large basket or carried over the shoulder, into the barn. Every now and then the mounting heap of cavings between the long riddle and straw elevator would be cleared, either into the elevator or thrown to make a separate heap.

Barley sheaves were best fed head first, and wheat straight across, especially when the straw was wanted for thatching. So with wheat the feeding was often done with a fork. Then a slipway was made over the feed hole and the band-cutter would throw the sheaves on to this for the feeder to pull in with a pitchfork. There was more to this than to drawing down first. Thick bunches had to be held back with a turn of the wrist and deft arm movement. Here much skill was required to prevent the engine governors dropping with every sheaf and a corresponding snappy exhaust note announcing the fault. An 'artist at the job' could pick a sheaf up with his fork and spread it like a pack of cards to dribble down into the ever hungry drum, like a thin golden film.

The two hours from 7am to 'lunch' at 9am always seemed the longest of the day and there was hunger too. The sheaves came up to be grasped, loosened and let-go with monotonous regularity. Sometimes there was a pause when the straw elevator stopped until the driver got there to tighten the belt, but this never lasted long.

As time went on, the mate's eye would increasingly turn with anxiety to the engine chimney to make sure that no black smoke from a recent firing-up was there, which would mean there was still some time to go before the stop. He much preferred to see a white plume, which meant a dropped damper. (With the ashpan lid closed no air was coming through the firebars, which lessened the hot gases drawn through the tubes by the exhaust steam, clearly indicated as the smoke rose from the chimney. Thus was steam being run down for the stop.)

At last would come the tap, tap, tap of the driver's hammer on the wheel, the rick men would stick in their forks and move towards the ladder and the mate signal when all was clear to stop. Then the drum would lower its note and soon the beaters give a final flit, flit, flit before coming to rest.

'Lunch' was really breakfast and the farm men's flat straw baskets would each reveal a loaf, cheese and an onion or two, which was cut into mouthfuls and knife-conveyed, to eat. Some had home-cured bacon, others a hunk from a Sunday joint, but red, thick-skinned cheese predominated. The enginemen more often had wicker rectangular baskets which fitted neatly onto a bicycle carrier and distinguished them from farm men. Theirs would contain sandwiches, and sometimes, tomatoes in place of onions. All had cold tea, which was drunk from the bottle, and could be warmed alongside the engine or made very hot indeed by laying in the crank-pit.

With only half an hour and all hungry, there was little talking. Boys were told that every time they spoke they lost a champ, so mouths were kept constantly full. Some ate standing, as if it was effeminate to sit down for such a brief interval.

At 9.30am the wheels would begin to turn again, the main belt flapping and trembling with every piston stroke before settling down to running speed, and soon all would be merrily in unison once more; the sheaves passing regularly from man to man; the drum note gently rising and falling as the feeder spread his sheaves, the engine be beating time to it all. The small belts would be clicking and clacking, the sounds sometimes catching up with each other then slowly parting, then coming together again. A similar game played between the rival cranks of riddles and shakers, the sieves in the one whispering and shuffling at 200rpm and a quiet rattle from the others at their 180, so nearly together, then syncopated, until quite-even-apart then the increasingly odd beats again until parity was reached and the cycle begun again.

At 10am, the driver's head would appear above the drum ladder and soon he would be in the feeding hole, with never a pause in the threshing, relieving the mate to go down below to the welcome change to keeping-steam. Coal would be barrowed, lifted into the bunker and the large lumps cracked, edge-on; the pump's adjustment varied if necessary; the farm cart with two tubs in it drained by the lifter pipe and the boy with it sent off for more. Every now and then three or four shovel-fulls would be put on the fire, wherever it was thinnest, and a wary eye kept on the whole tackle meanwhile. The straw elevator would sometimes need winding higher and when the chaff-man was too slow in returning to clear the cavings these would have a push through to prevent the caving riddle being blocked. Thistle heads and straw chibblings coming over the bottom sieve into a tin bath had to be watched less it tipped-up and blocked the sieve. The sack-man might nod to be relieved for a while, and so might the band-cutter, who liked a quiet smoke on the engine every now and then, when it was set to run for a while without attention. This man, of course, knew well enough how to shut the regulator should anything go wrong. An embryo mate, cum thrashing-machine-follower, a going-from-job-to-job man, he who cut bands generally differed from the farmer's own men.

Many engines had an iron ring at the top of their chimney, and other new ones generally a flared top, copper or brass and varying in shape according to the make. If the engine had a top on it the mate generally cleaned it; the best way being to rub round with the piece of sacking first oiled and dipped in the fine ash which accumulated behind the damper lid. This scoured off the discoloration caused by heat and weather, and it soon shone up then after a rub with a soft rag. What could not be reached by standing on the footboard was finished from the drum's ladder, not without getting a whiff of hot smoke now and then. The smokebox end boiler brass (three and sometimes four $2\frac{1}{2}$in brass bands went round to keep the lagging in place) would also be cleaned with ashes, with metal polish being used on the adjacent cooler ones. Polish went too on steam gauge, regulator rod, and whistle, the latter seldom used its valve often screwed tight to prevent dribbling. The driver would polish the connecting rod and link bars in the dinner interval. After polishing, everything was oiled, which made it easier for next time, and the parts did not look any the worse—more engine-like, somehow.

But being down below was not all work. Pleasant indeed was it to watch the threshing scene from the footplate. On a still day one could 'write one's mark on the sky' after firing up. And the golden straw filling the creeping elevator dropped intermittently, in showering cascades. There it heaped on the rick for the man standing near it to get a good forkfull to slide along to the rick-builder who carefully placed it to maintain a shape. Or one could sit on the bunker plate and watch the pump chirruping and clucking its own little ditty which varied with the tap's setting. After a long and tiring bout of feeding, the pump could have a mesmeric effect, and send a man nodding, once comfortably seated on the flanged-over bunker divide.

Towards twelve o'clock the mate returned to feeding and the last hour to dinner time soon passed. Fewer men were around in that period, some going home. After finishing what was left in their bags those who stayed would get themselves comfortable on sheaves and some would doze. The mate spent ten minutes of his hour on filling the oiler on the shaker and riddle cranks, while the driver would cut off straw wound round moving parts of the elevator; oil his engine;

make a few adjustments round it and the tackle, and sometimes sweep the tubes. These were 1¾in or 2in and generally 32 in number. The cylindrical wire brush on its long handle had to go right through before it could be drawn back (unless it was worn) and a little smoking soot, acrid and sometimes glowing came through each time, to be carefully swept into a half-bucket of water and tipped well away. Poor coal and light barley threshing made a daily sweep necessary; otherwise twice a week was enough.

At 2pm the main belt would once more begin to flap, and slip a little over the drum pulley before taking up its load for the afternoon. Then things would continue as before, with the driver coming up to relieve the mate from 3pm until 4pm.

As 5pm approached the drum's note would lower as the driver began to run down steam by putting the pump full on. If the glass was not topped up by the time the belt came off and there was no injector, or steam pressure was too low for it, the engine would be gently run by itself while the banking-up lumps of coal were thrown on. Then with practised speed would the sheets be rolled over drum and engine and the drum ladder left against the chimney so that the top (or lid) could be placed on, with a spud there to keep it firm.

It was easy to pick out a driver and mate as men walked away from a tackle, as they most times wore blue overalls, with separate jacket and trousers. Few farm men would presume to wear this uniform unless they, at some time or other, had also been engine-men: then it was usually the top half only. Mates, particularly new ones, were generally the blacker of the two. This was because they had yet to learn not to touch their faces, no matter how the threshing dust caused an itch, as hands were coal besmudged and oily and only when these had been cleaned with soft soap under a dribbling injector could they so indulge.

A driver had to be really ill to stay away from work, as few liked anyone else to tamper with their engine. But in such intervals the mate drew in know-how like an empty tank sucking in water. With the mate on the footplate, it was the band-cutter's turn to pull out the belt and gauge the length when setting, and many times did the new driver have to climb down and back again for a check—and many shunts too had to be made when the ground was wet before the engine got in-line enough for the belt to run. 'Near enough' was then the rule if the farmer was waiting to start: 'plumb in the middle' had to wait for adjustments at the next meal break, which was quite used up with the double lot of oiling, and experimenting with sieve and blower adjustments. There was no time to eat until threshing was again in progress, so the band-cutter-turned-feeder had but little time down below.

When on the road a good temporary driver would err on the slow side so as not to overheat a bearing. And he'd block up—himself if need be—and change down to low gear at every steep hill, the engine being easier to control then, slowing with less lever-holding beyond the centre. He would probably have to steer as well as drive, as, by a combination of tradition and diffidence, the band-cutter, who was usually seated well back on the elevator could seldom be persuaded to come forward and even then preferred sitting on the jolting bunker with only a rolled sack between him and disintegration. Before developing his own style, it was as well to base his method's on the absent driver's. Too brash an approach, as could be seen when mates were promoted with too little training and discipline behind them, seldom led to the quiet and professional attitude of a good driver. Much noise and rapid revving, with needless time spent spinning the steering wheel and shunting to and fro was a sad contrast to careful motion-studied moves where things fell into place with ease.

An exercise in forethought was a pull-back to two adjacent stacks. Chains should be out and ready, and spuds on if necessary before the drum stopped running. It was as well not to have too much steam pressure then, as the engine would be snatchy, not stopping at the precise moment; frustrating when half-way up tapered blocks in front to improve a head-down belt position, and soon sliding off or going over the top then, without the utmost care and control of crank movement by regulator-and-lever, with body against the steering wheel to keep it steady. Should the steam be too low, however, with sticky or steep manoeuvring ahead, there was always plenty of oiling, or drum wingboard fixing to do until the needle had lifted enough. Trying a move without sufficient steam could cause priming, stalling and a strain on tempers.

Before becoming a fully fledged threshing driver a mate would benefit from some other form of experience. Being a countryman he was likely to think about steam ploughing, and let his fancy dwell there. The season for this was busiest between threshing times and, apart from an autumnal lap, could be fitted in well.

Things heard and seen from a distance can have a magnetism, steam ploughs especially. Early morning whistles; the staccato barks of singles at first-time-over on a fallow—sometimes coming nearly to a stop, then speeding to a roar on a piece of easy going only to steady-up again as the drag's tines go into clay or claw through a stony patch; or the majestic compounds, panting like mastiffs, louder or quieter with the varying ground but seldom varying in speed. And on the road, the deep toned ring of the large gear wheels, rising and falling, merging and parting; first one engine, then an echo of the other, then the two together, then an echo, and a fading solo again, could be as melancholy as distant church bells and as faint as the memory of them.

6 Steam Ploughing

Steam plough owners had to cater for irregular seasons, and the good ones were when the ground was too dry and hard for the farmer to tackle. For fallowing when the field was often left until choked with weeds, there was nothing to beat the steam plough. The ground would be dragged through one way, leaving large lumps. These were broken and any untouched bits found by crossing it as near to right-angles as possible, at the same time dragging the weeds to the top die.

When the more powerful compound engines were available—they were few before 1900—which had worm and chain-roller steering, clutch-on-the-vertical-shaft, second-speed control by lever and up to 800yd of wire rope—many owners bought as large a size as could be manoeuvred. A compound enabled more work to be done more economically with the same set of men and greater advantage could be taken of a favourable season, when orders came in faster than they could be executed.

It was best that at least one man—generally the foreman—should have been brought up in the trade from boyhood. Such key men were carefully hoarded out of season, and in a wet summer general repairs of all sorts of agricultural implements would be undertaken, so as to keep them employed. A trained steam plough driver or second man was an advantage too. The other three in the team would generally be casuals, although many of these came back to the same set, season after season.

A steam ploughman started his life as a boy cook, looking after the others' requirements. The five and six berth vans had stoves and there was always plenty of coal around. Eggs, meat, milk, tea, bread, butter and so on could always be bought from the nearest village and some sort of meal supplemented by the men's own rations from home, prepared every evening as well as fried breakfasts and handkerchief bound snacks brought out to the field. In fine weather, work never stopped between daylight and sunset, so the cook was kept busy enough. If interested, he would pick up much engine lore from the others, learn the art of splicing a wire rope and help in a multiplicity of field repairs. Sometimes he would be allowed to steer on the road and often take a turn on the cultivator (or scuffle). The more skilled guidance of the six-furrowed anti-balance plough was seldom allowed him in his first year. But keen observation at this most impressionable time taught him much.

The foreman's engine was generally, but not always, the left-hand—the name taken from the side on which the rope came out—the other being the 'driver's engine'. The spare driver, or third man, drove the foreman's engine when the latter had his meals or relieved the driver to have his, or did the many things needed of a foreman. Foremen varied, of course. Some having a good spare driver, would practically give him the engine and spend their time on the implement, particularly if the plough was much in use. Others would drive all day and never let anyone touch their engine, so that all the practice the third man had was on the right-hand engine, unless that driver too was selfish and ate his meals on the footplate between pulls. When there was a shortage of drivers—not all third men could properly master the art of driving—this procedure was the rule.

A good foreman would train the cook-boy if he saw intelligence and keenness, by letting him stand beside him whenever he could. Later he would leave him on his own for a few pulls, coming back periodically to cast an eye over steam and water gauges. Boys such as these who showed beyond doubt that they were devoted to the job were kept on out of season by the owners. Personality came into it too. A potential foreman had to be able to control men and deal tactfully with opinionated farmers and would have to go through the stages of being drag-man and the driver of the right-hand engine before taking the top job.

Unless it was a slack season, when crews would be telescoped, the spare driver was often an outsider, there just for the season. Good and competent he might be, but unless he had gone through the earlier stages, he was never a steam ploughman. However, he was generally welcome. It was not necessary for him to learn how to splice a rope, or the best way to begin a field, assess acreages, to know how many 'tines' to have on the scuffle frame, or how to set a plough. All he had to do was drive in the field, that is if he was a steam man of some sort; and steer on the road. Sometimes he would

even drive on the road, with the cook steering. Ploughing engines
were surprisingly easy to manage then, being over-powered for their
load and with a great amount of footplate room. Firing up was not so
frequent or difficult as with the harder working threshing engine
with its proportionately heavy tackle behind.

The threshing mate was easy to train as third man. Here again
the foreman would have him up beside him for a time later, and
keep a careful eye on him. The mate would discover how easy the
short reverse lever was to move, in spite of the two sets of links. The
regulator too was a delight, the straight-up handle in just the right
position, letting steam into the chest more gently than anything he
had been used to. This, he was told, was because the opening in the
steam chest was heart-shaped instead of square, the narrow end
being uncovered first. The long road-gear handle was close to the
reversing lever, and on the other side, outside the frame, an up-and-
down lever controlled a one-way dog clutch on the vertical-shaft,
bevel driven from the crank shaft, the flywheel being dished to make
room for the driven bevel. 'Up' was in gear, and if the engine was
reversed it would slip out itself and only need gentle pressure 'down'
to latch it out. Triggered out of its notch and pressed down beyond,
it worked a brake to steady or stop the rope drum from running
round on its own when free. The top half of the vertical shaft was
always turning, via the bevels and the bottom half remained inert
when out of gear or unclutched (earlier singles engaged by sliding
the crankshaft-bevel in and out of mesh with the one on the vertical
shaft).

To begin a pull a wisp of steam was given with a light hand on the
regulator, when the two cranks would slowly turn, 'over-over,
balance-balance, over-over, balance-balance' (the cranks, as on all
compounds being set at right angles and their balance weights at
180° to each. These were generally painted red and looked fine when
the sun glinted on polished big-end oil cups, dipping down and
coming up between them). The reverse lever would be forward on a
left-hand engine with links down and the flywheel revolving in a
threshing direction—clockwise from the near side. Next the rope-
drum lever would be lifted until the clutch 'clunked' in. With practice, regulator and rope lever could be moved together. Next a gentle
little tug at the regulator so as to turn the implement at the other
end of the field as steadily as possible, then, as the load was felt this
could be opened up when the closeness of the heavy gears' noise
tended to drown the soft panting of compound-exhaust.

The revs could be surprising, due to the better balance of the compound, aided by the foreman's constant attention to motion adjustments and wick-feeds. The flywheel with its bulging curved spokes was more than 4ft 6in on the largest engine, and made more massive to withstand the centrifugal force. It was soon easy to realise why compounds were popular for this kind of work as they were so often flat-out on second-time-over, revving hard; and on the first bout too, although slower, would be needing all their horsepower with an occasional touch on the 'double-high'—to let live steam into the low pressure cylinder—where the ground conditions became stiffer. It was easy to see why single cylindered engines were little used when compounds came in. The harder exhaust caused more wear-and-tear on smokebox and chimney plating, and their jerkiness led to a need for more maintenance; also, having no second crank, it was not so well balanced, which reduced its speed. A Single, working hard, could be heard miles away, its exhaust beats coming out 'like square blocks', while a compound merely 'chutted'.

Towards the end of a pull, a slowing-down was required, so that when the stop came the other engine's rope-drum would not be left spinning without a tight rope. Loose, it would drop from its coiled position, and if wound-on then, became distorted and kinky. A dropped rope had to be put back in its place with the coiling bar, a hard and time-consuming job. Steam plough ropes had 'life' or spring in them, and could only be put on in the first place under load, generally by pulling the other engine along, out of gear.

Coiling gear, worked from underneath the rope-drum, moved an arm with a pair of vertical pulleys at its end slowly up and down, a rope's width at each turn of the drum, to guide the incoming rope. It was free to swing in a horizontal plane to allow for the various angles of pull. Sometimes on a bending headland too great a turn towards the line of pull would cause the rope to catch the front wheel, as often the grooves there would testify.

Immediately the engine came to rest, the reversing lever was pulled back, when steam remaining in the chest would usually be enough to turn it backwards releasing the rope-driven clutch and allowing the road-gear lever to be slipped in at the same time. If not, with this gear not 'fitting', the reverse lever would be put forward and a touch of the regulator given until it did. There was then an implement width, forward movement, so as to be ready for the next pull.

Meanwhile, the paying-out rope drum would be clink-clunking, as its brake rotated with it, agitating the ratchet there. The steering wheel would then be twisted to aim it correctly and to avoid leaning back to reach it when the next short move forward came. On a bend the regulator could be left to its own devices to keep the engine turning, while a step back was made and both hands put on the wheel.

When the pupil had grasped the rudiments, further instruction would be given on co-ordination, until at last there was no pause between the end of a pull and the move forward. When out of the road-gear the cranks would lob over gently with a pleasing sound until all the steam in the cylinders had gone. Sometimes after a long and hard pull it was as well to keep them turning over for a while to get a little oil back on the piston rods and into the cylinders, where the effort had dried them. During such a pull a shovel of coal could be put on, although closer attention to the fire came when the other engine was pulling.

As compounds could only give of their best at maximum pressure, the ideal was to have the safety valves lifting as soon as the regulator was eased. There was plenty of room in the boiler then for a good injection of water to silence the blowing-off and prevent waste (there was seldom pumps on ploughing engines). It was as well to start a pull with as full a glass as possible whether head-up, level, or head-down even if it lowered the steam. With clean bars and good coal the needle would soon lift again with some steady pulling for a time, and occasional assistance from the auxiliary valve.

When the spare driver became competent on the left-hand engine he would take over the foreman's meal-time turn on the right-hand one, and learn that the difference between them was greater than just having the lever back and links up, to pull. Apart from having a different stance, with left hand on the regulator, and a slight variation in 'drill', the engine itself, identical in appearance, would often differ in all sorts of minor ways, which could be felt when handling it. And one engine was frequently a better steamer than the other for no apparent reason. Thus he would realise that no twins are ever alike, no matter how similar in appearance.

Ploughing engines made good use of their whistles, one being to signal the 'other driver' to stop when an implement in trouble was hidden from his view: or to liven him up if he had ignored the drag man's hand signal. Another whistle expressed urgency to the farmer's team with the water cart. This was a large high mounted end-on cylindrical tank with a hand suction pump which emptied by gravity to the engine's tanks. Usually two or three horses drew it and courtesy was always shown when it wanted to cross a line of pull. No delay was permitted with the water cart, as empty engine tanks earned no acreage bonus!

Washing out was an exciting event. Instead of the monthly Sunday morning chore when threshing, where the boiler was emptied from a bottom mud-hole-lid, with as much saved as possible in tubs and a low tank, the engines 'did it themselves', saving much carrying of buckets and funnelling in from the top. First they would get as near as they could to a stream or clean pond. Then the fire would be thrown out of one engine with an injector left on until it faded off for lack of pressure. Steam would then be let off from every tap-opening to lower the pressure still further. At about 25lb the foreman would start undoing a large tapered plug in the front corner of the firebox base, with a long box spanner, leaving it half undone until steam and water spurting past the threads dropped the pressure to between 5 and 10lb. Then he would give it the last turn. With a roar, steam, water, mud and scale would shoot out and blow the plug forward—to be stopped by a held-up board—until after a couple of minutes, silence reigned again. A flexible pipe would next be uncoiled and screwed to a union under the boiler feed pipe of the other engine, so that by using its injector, water under pressure could scour where mud and impurities were likely to lodge. When the water running through the bottom man-holes ran clear, these and the corner-plug would be replaced and the pipe put in the top opening to fill the boiler. Fire from the live engine would then be transferred, and because the water was nearly boiling, not much time would elapse before steam was up. Meanwhile the second engine would be similarly prepared and the procedure repeated.

All engines ran the better for a wash-out. It was unpleasant to see mud in a glass and never a clear top to the water in it. Too dirty a boiler always meant some priming which, by scoring piston and valve surfaces would lead to loss of economy and power.

A dedicated driver—and most were, or such hard and dirty work with long hours and irregular meals would seldom be undertaken— found much satisfaction in steam ploughing. From where he stood, his own engine did not seem so dramatic, just chimney, steam-chest and big-ends. But by looking across at the other, its long boiler glistening and rods above it flashing to and fro, the flywheel spokes a blur and black smoke from its set-back chimney shooting straight up into the summer sky he would be seeing himself as in a mirror, and begin to fire-up for the next pull with gusto.

It was never a smooth ride on the scuffle, particularly first-time-over. The shimmering rope ahead would whip and tremble and progress be in great jerks as the ground cracked and split ahead of the deep clawing tines and came up in huge lumps behind. The scuffle's frame was supported by a pair of high wheels with a box-lid seat between and a large straight down steering wheel which only chain-guided its heavy frontwheel effectively at a distance for as the rope in front shortened its control decreased. The rope pulled from one arm of a large 'V' straight ahead in line with it, while the other trailed the paying-out rope. On the turn, with the latter starting to pull, the other arm of the 'V' became straight and the movement lifted the scuffle by a linkage out of the ground before it started to turn it round. When in line again, the dragman pulled a long lever in front of his wheel to drop the frame, steadied down by a rod which ran back into a long narrow cylinder full of oil. (A generation later something similar was re-invented for aircraft legs. A second re-invention was the chisel plough hailed also as something new, but only really a replica of the scuffle or a drag modified to do similar work from behind a tractor.)

The less often used anti-balance plough had six furrows, a straight across steering wheel and a guiding wheel behind and was supported, like the scuffle, by two large wheels in front. Beyond these the frame angled up and sideways a little, carrying six more furrows and a steering wheel. This end was pulled down by the dragman when the wire rope tightened from the opposite direction, and when the sideways slant did not fit into the edge of the last bout he could easily swing it there. Sometimes then he had to give a short run to catch it up, grasping his new steering wheel to swing into the fresh seat while crumbs of soil ran off the shiny surface of the other, now above him. It was better if two men were on the plough, the second sitting on the end to keep it in and helping with the pulling down. Sometimes the cook would do this intermittently, at others a farmer's man came along. The farmer himself was seldom popular then.

A field steam-ploughed had the then unique appearance of all the furrows leaning one way instead of being in neat pieces with one block of furrows one way and one the opposite, as was necessary with horse and tractor ploughs. (Again a re-invention of a system came with the present-day turn-over ploughs, which have idle furrows on top to twist round at the headland.)

Those with steam ploughing 'in their blood' always had the 'magnetism of distance' with them; the implement was seldom

close-up and the other engine mostly far away. They developed an
upright stance; a straining to look into the distance, which, when
added to a foreman's authority gave a dignity seldom seen among
'working men'—as they were apt to call themselves. With a weather-
beaten face and keen eye this gave a Red Indian look to some; while
stouter ones, who became so, they said, "due to the oxygen in the
soil" could appear kings indeed when seated on the scuffle, relaxed
and calm, no matter how it jerked and swayed.

Such men could never see a field without wondering "how they
would get their engines in". "Backed through, of course", if the gate
was near the roadside, "and keeping going backwards then, pulling
the other man's rope out across the field for the start." A long down-
slope of headland from a starting point could mean "taking it backwards", so as to keep water over the fireboxes; and low branches in a
line of advance would be mentally snitched off by the long chain,
which hung, with the 'two hooks' on the back of the bunker. A white
roof almost hidden behind a cluster of straight trees could look in
imagination mightily like steam from a safety valve; and sometimes
a spinney, low down on the far end of a cropless field, would seem
specially there to have black smoke puthering through from engines
coming in that end to start cultivating! Steam ploughing stayed
with a man, no matter how long ago he had left it.

However—with autumn's approach, when the faint hum of a
threshing drum could be heard here and there the thoughts of many
a man with a ploughing set would turn to ricks and straw and the
pleasures of a bed instead of a van-bunk. There would be some worry
from dragmen and cooks about what they were going to do in the
approaching winter; perhaps become band-cutters or even threshing
mates if the steam plough owner did not want them to help his
blacksmith as a striker, or knock the scale off boiler tubes. Drivers
had less anxiety, particularly the spare driver, who had 'done a bit
of threshing' before.

7 A Return to Threshing

Although threshing and steam ploughing seasons overlapped both were at their peak just after harvest. A spare driver with the 'ploughers' who wanted to get away could be replaced by another man to fit in anywhere as the days got shorter, and later on four could manage. This left the foreman to drive most of the time and often short stops were then made for meal breaks.

The threshing mate-cum-spare ploughing engine driver would now be sufficiently experienced to be trusted with a threshing set of his own, and then how small did his new footplate seem; how close the steering wheel and how snatchy the regulator! He would not of course get the best set, and often too much of the type of work no-one else wanted, like 'bat tying'—where a straw trusser replaced the elevator—and threshing-and-cutting.

A trusser meant a frequent running round to the straw end—where most of the dust was—to fiddle with the knotters. A reaper-and-binder's knotter rarely gave trouble, as it worked in the open field. But the loose straws and dust were apt to put this delicate mechanism out of order; also there were two knotters instead of one, and the larger and less dense straw bundles could disrupt the throwing-out mechanism. Added to this the pitching man had only to be away for a minute and the revolving forks might lift a truss left there, taking it round with them on the way to throw out the next one. This would either break a link in the flimsy chain drive, or cause the crossed belt to the shakers—from where it took its drive—to come off, and this left long unnoticed could bung up the thresher. But for sheer hard work both for driver and engine nothing could beat threshing-and-cutting.

In the days of horses there was a chaff-cutter in most stables. A handle turned a wheel on which was a pair of curved blades and the wheel also worked toothed rollers. These drew in straw, fed length-ways in a narrow trough, which the blades cut into $\frac{1}{2}$in lengths, and

56

and the straw had to be tightly pressed down otherwise the rollers could not grasp it properly. Here was the beginnings of a skill, the feeder finding that once 'drawing', the rollers instead of his pressing, would do the compacting too as they drew in, as long as he could get the entering straw to overlap. This he did by shuffling the top layer back a little with his left hand and gently pressing towards the rollers with his right at every armful.

The steam chaff-cutter was a development of this. The wheel, now carrying five knives, was encased and its shaft run through to the opposite end on which was a 2ft 6in driven pulley. Chain drive slats in the trough aided the straw's progress towards the pressing rollers and disintegration, with the cut lengths (or chaff) falling onto a sieve which slid off the long pieces and let the rest through to a wide cup-elevator, also wood encased, with its delivery-end at sack height from the ground. Two long sacks were hung here so that when one was full a change-over slat would direct the material to the other. The sack man had to be quick and the carriers nimble on their feet to keep up, they themselves often looking like walking heaps of chaff because of what stuck to them when emptying, generally in a loft above the mangers.

This machine began its life in the days when there were plenty of men on the farm. It would be set besides a straw rick, generally oat straw, and sometimes hay, and be driven by the farmer's portable engine. Men on the rick would fork towards the feeder who gathered the armfulls, or yealms, and overlapped it through; with a good man serving him the straw appeared to come off the rick in one continuous roll. If it went through too thickly a safety pin holding a gear wheel to its shaft would break and the feeding mechanism then stop. This would mean a hold-up and it was not always easy to punch the broken parts of the pin out, bent-over ends sometimes delaying a straight tap through.

He who first thought of threshing-and-cutting was deemed not worthy of a medal but of being threshed-and-cut himself! A cutter driven from the drum* in place of the light running elevator or tyer was much harder work for the engine, and the driver had twice as much coal breaking and firing, and the blades on the spare knife-wheel to sharpen too. He did this with a flat file, and as the blades were not deep enough for a full stroke the file was broken off in sections as it wore down and jabbing the last bit up and down with fingers close to the blade was at some risk. Occasionally a stone or

* A 6in wide belt came off a flanged extension to the main drum-pulley.

piece of metal would be cut up with the chaff. This could take a segment out, and there were usually several of these which had to be sharpened around their crescent edges; sometimes the blade was merely hardened where it had hit, and although it did not look so bad, was even more difficult to sharpen, and a new piece of file often kept by especially for these, which were apt to stand-out leaving a wavy edge, as the rest of the blade wore down with filing. As blades were slightly angled inwards and for the best results had just to touch the face, wavy ones either bore too hard or did not touch. The cure was removing and grinding them to shape, but so often were holding screws impossible to move and adjusting studs bent over or broken off, that this job was rarely tackled on the farm. Chaff cutters seemed particularly prone to thread corrosion, possibly because the short bits and extra dust adhered more closely, allowing acids and rust to do their worst in the longer periods of standing. The length of time a knife would run before it had to be changed varied with the sort of crop being dealt with, but two hours was an average, and nothing was gained by keeping them on too long and nearly stopping the engine as a result, to say nothing of the extra filing afterwards.

The man feeding the cutter—usually the mate, with the band-cutter up-graded for feeding the drum and a farm man cutting bands—was always in the dust and often wore a handkershief over nose and mouth. There were times when the straw came over the shakers too fast for him to handle, when, as the drum feeder was hidden from view, he had to attract the attention of the men on the rick. Thus a pause could seldom be at once, and in the interval he would duck and slide surplus straw over his shoulders, getting eyes and ears full of bits and husks. It has not been unknown for a frustrated man to over-feed and break a pin, then.

A further development was a blower to take the chaff away. This was a large fan in a figure-six shaped casing, into which the chaff went from the sieve. It had a 4in pulley driven by a belt from an extension to the cutter's main pulley. This went at nearly twice the drum speed, and required more power still to drive it. A $4\frac{1}{2}$in diameter thin gauge metal pipe with a bend in it slipped over the tail of the casing, and from there, piping continued in yard lengths with hinge and clip joints. Sacking was wrapped and tied round these to keep the air in, and the assembly kept up by three or four pairs of what looked like crossed line-props all the way to the loft, fifteen yards being about as far as the chaff would blow out clear.

A blower was an added task for the driver too. A slipping belt between the drum and cutter, or cutter and blower, or a combination of both would lower the note of the moaning fan, causing him to drop everything and rush there to prevent its slowing, as if this went on long the pipes would bung. The belt from the drum might stand a bit more tightening by a turn of the large racked-jack set against the cutter's frame; or some belt stick be put on the blower belt, as should this be overtightened the fan bearing would get hot: risky with combustible material about. A bung meant an unauthorised stop, which never failed to aggravate the farmer, with his men idle and waiting. The driver, mate and bandcutter would then dismantle the ragged line of pipes, tipping each one up to empty. When there was a cold wind to swirl the chaff from these around and freeze the fingers as they retied the sacking over joints, a wise farmer would muffle his annoyance.

Most blowers had a low ground clearance and most double doors and gates a mid stump to close on. When the farmer's men fetched the cutter by horses, when left three or four farms back, it could happen that the former collided with the latter. Many a driver's heart has sunk on seeing a resulting 'cow-jawed' blower. Only rarely was a levering-back with iron bar one side and push pole the other an effective cure. Often fan blades would be damaged and their holding brackets moved. This would put the blower out of balance and cause damaging vibration. An emergency 'bodge-up' involving both cold-iron-blacksmithing and clasp-knife-carpentering could, however, work wonders, especially if a sense of urgency was great enough.

Even a 7nhp single had its hands full when threshing-and-cutting-and-blowing. The exhaust bark was continuous and unrelieved by a governor-lifting, and towards the end of a knife run, as the pulling got harder, the black lead and oil on smokebox and chimney would blister and crack. For this a piece of sacking well soaked in thick cylinder oil was kept on the front wheel ready for a daub round now and then to keep the plates from burning. Boiler pressure had to be 'well up' all the time, so that at each unauthorised stop, and there could be many on an unlucky day, a noisy blowing-off from the safety valves, would follow.

Seldom did driver and mate have more than minutes for food. At the meal breaks, there would be the cutter to oil as well as the drum; belt tensions to check; extra coal to heave and crack; extra clinkers to draw if the coal was dusty; and always a knife-wheel to change— first the large holding nut to be clouted loose with the long handled spanner on it; then the clamp to ease it away from the tapered shaft; a two-man ease-down to the ground and a three man heave-up with the new wheel, after a tortuous wheel-down from the engine, near where it had been sharpened. The usual practice was to keep it upright against a rear wheel by a bent bar spiked into the ground. No cleaning was done on those days, and the engine would look a rare mess with chaff and dust covering the motion and sticking on every oily part and the chimney red with rust here and there on the belt side where the oil daubs could not reach. The mate's spells were shorter: ten minutes or so now and then to cough out some dust and take a swill of tea, and as a reward for this he had to replenish the bunker. Keeping steam meant fleeting footplate visits to fire-up, a cursory glance at the water-level, a twitch of pump tap and a little ash-pan raking now and then. With the everlasting sharpening and being always on the run, the engine had to suffer some neglect.

Farmers, like the old sailing ship captains, were sometimes 'hard cases', and, stimulated by the sight of such activity on the part of the enginemen would often chivvy their own men around. A new sack-man was once observed to be working non-stop, unencouraged, as it were. "Others might need it", he observed, "but not me, I've been well trained. At my last place I had to go shepherding all night after a day's farm work, and even then the boss would be on to me to dig his garden in my dinner hour."

Clover hulling was another unpleasantness. Few men could get used to the sort of dust from this, black, choking and eye filling. The huller was a different kind of thresher, smaller, but with two drums, one for threshing off the clover heads and the other, of fibrous material, for rubbing the seed out of them. Hulling or 'Rubbing' was mostly a winter's job, and when the rick was mouldy from a late harvest, the mildew would rise from the men's forks, like mist. The short thick straws compacted into layers and it was gruelling work peeling these off and trying to get them up to the feeder in segments, otherwise, there was poking and wrist twisting to keep anything on the fork at all. The feeder had a strenuous time shaking the material out before he could persuade it down the drum and it would often hang long on the shakers, with dust from them rising in billowing clouds.

The drum's note was pitched higher than a grain thresher's, so that if the feeder—still breathing down his nose (and what a good dust filter this was)—made his mouth an 'O' the noise would 'dong' pleasantly through his head, and by varying his 'O' he could get two higher notes and one lower in harmony with the basic one. The ditty was as simple as a bugle call, but helpful.

The straw elevator was seldom used, its rakes being designed for longer stalks. So a pile was left to accumulate shaker-high and forked from there into more of a heap than a rick, with dust in every movement. Dust also puthered from the chaff spout and every crack and corner, and a wind towards the engine left this as if clothed in velvet.

The pin-head sized seed needed careful dressing, so that the engine had to be kept at a constant speed—a steady steam gauge needle ensured this—and the fan shutters regulated carefully. The farmer would be as pleased as his calling allowed him to be, if five sacks a day came off. (Farmers were rarely 'jolly'!) A compensation in hulling was that it filled gaps between orders for ordinary threshing, there was less tackle to move about and longer stays at a setting.

High winds could be a bugbear to threshing, blowing chaff and dust into many an unaccustomed eye, but the enginemen were only concerned when the straw would not stay in the elevator, lest it bring all to a stop.

Heavy rain did this as damp corn went mouldy, nor would exposed belts keep on for long even if the men were willing to work in the wet; but a drizzle could do no more than make the driver tighten the jack against his wheel to keep the main belt on, and if it still slipped, hold a rolled sack against the under-belt as it ran towards the drum pulley. Thus until the drum's note could no longer be prevented from lowering, the team were likely to keep going, as the casual men and the threshing time were only paid for when working. Many farmers were unwilling to take the thatch off a new rick if rain was in the offing, and some used this as an excuse to escape to market or avoid starting up on a Saturday. Thus did a driver need all his persuasive powers, and sometimes threats to move on to the next farm, before a start would be made. Competition was keen, and a delay on one farm could mean losing the custom of the next. On a showery day a spud would be hung on the lower half of the belt at meal times and so only presenting its edge to the wet; the drum sheet would be rolled back over the top, and the farm men would spread a layer of straw over their workings.

A driver's ways were not always understood by the mate, who sometimes wondered at all the hurry. But he had to get in as many days a week as was possible, and keep a waiting list of farmers faithful. Apart from normal competition there was a growing risk, as tractors came in, that customers would get a drum of their own. Even before the days of rubber tyres a tractor could drive a drum very well and provided it did not have to traverse roads and fields, proved adequate in the farmyard.

A hundred days' threshing before Christmas was deemed a good average. As these got shorter and the weather worsened, and orders began to be spaced out, there was seldom more than another fifty done before the season's end, in late March or early April. There would sometimes be a few ricks here and there until May or June, by which time they became very dusty and verminous. By then mates would be hoeing roots or haymaking and drivers would go out together in pairs for an odd day or two a week. Wood sawing would occupy some engines; while the 'spare driver' could go back to ploughing or take a newer type of summer's job, like dragging a tar-boiler along, with a threshing engine, while chippings or gravel was spread behind it, for yet another threshing-driver to follow with a steam roller.

With accumulated experience less notice was taken of temporary hardship and less anxiety felt as the answers to things began to get clearer. This was particularly so of a driver fond of taking things to pieces and putting them together again, and who could do a little wood-work. These would be repairing and overhauling in the between seasons. No longer, then, would chaff-cutter blades go hit and miss. Plenty of time, handy drills, taps and dies would cure this and many other things. Riddle and shaker big-end bearings would be relieved of thump and rattle; some small belts replaced, and top boards made secure again after getting shaky from daily openings and shuttings, and twistings from uneven loading. Then would follow a wash-down with soda-softened warm water and, if the paint was good, an overall varnishing. If re-painting was needed this was generally done in salmon-pink with chassis and beams in deep red.

Engines were rarely painted. Their works' livery, like wine in old bottles, seeming to improve and mellow as time went on. Should painting have been tried something was lost, and they were deemed to be like those who dyed their hair or wore wigs to disguise their age —age at that time being more honoured than feared. If an engine 'ran quiet and chipped it off nicely and the tube ends in the smoke-box were all the same length and gauge, and the steam pressure had not been brought down' there was not much wrong with it, no matter how old, although those who overhauled them had plenty to do to keep them that way. The odd patch or two was no detraction, nor was a dent in the lagging towards the front under-belly where the front wheel touched, when lifting in full lock. (Later engines had a stop on the centre pin to prevent too full a lock.) Threshing engines could go from father to son and even grandson, and provided there was not much road work and threshing-and-cutting was limited, there seemed no reason why they should not go on for ever; so many never even leaving the small cluster of farms around a village.

With anxiety getting less other things came into focus (like the steam ploughman's seeing himself, as it were, in the other man across the field). This was so when the smoke was puthering up from behind a neighbouring farm, thick and black with every firing, then thinning and greying as it shaped itself to the bordering poplar trees, with later the top of an elevator above a roof followed by a fringe of yellow rick to crown the slates below, peaceful and idyllic, yet the driver there could doubtless tell of troubles enough, from leaking tubes, to an out-of-balance drum.

There were times when things took on a very special significance, so that the shovel, lying half full in the bunker, gently oscillating in time with the engine, would cast distorted shadows on lumps of coal and reveal the rust and pitting on its handle, and, on a turn-round, the copper chimney top would smile back knowingly, its expression changing as the smoke wreathed round. Looking ahead along the top of the incoming main belt to the half red, half dusty front face of the drum, jogging with its riddles' movement, with gold-shot sheaves above and grey sacks below one could then detect, momentarily, a new and magic dimension. All around would be the rich deep hum, interspersed by the 'tickle-tockle, tickle-tockle' of the small belts as their fasteners raced over the pulleys. The note would slowly rise and fall, with the engine governors lifting and lowering with it and the time-beating coming in greater and lesser emphasis from the chimney. A double beat, one slightly the heavier, at 160 or so to the minute. If the sheaves came off easily, the first man would time them, one to every four engine beats, as he passed to the next, and this one along, or up, to the bandcutter. This rhythm sometimes lasted minutes before someone broke the sequence. And all the time the straw would be creeping upwards filling the elevator trough and heaping on the rick for a slowly moving high stepping man with reversed fork to pull down and pass along to another who placed and shaped and trod.

Well was it then to stand on the footplate and soak in the rhythm of it all, especially if the day was still and frosty, with the smoke going straight up and no dust coming that way to mar shining brass and flashing rods. And should a boiler-wash-out have been but recent then, perfection would reign, as the water in the glass would have an unblurred top, the valve rod would move with no thought of a jerk and all would be sweet smelling around.

'With muddy water, glands will scour,
Priming comes and steam is sour.'

8 Non-agricultural Engines

Showmen

A popular recreation of threshing and steam ploughmen was attending fairs at weekends. But not for them the galloping horses, the dodgems, the shooting galleries and other ways of lightening a purse. They preferred to be near the engines, (and from where some soon wore a path to the nearest pub)—the high standing spring mounted three-speed compound engines with twirled awning supports and chimney protruding through the extension over the dynamo in front of it. It was especially good when there were half a dozen or more. Then the different designs and ways they were worked came properly into focus. After absorbing this they would tend to stand by a favourite one, surrendering to the hypnotic effect of its throbbing rhythm on the background music from mechanical organs. The very large 10nhps with a second generator behind the chimney were the most magnificent. Going at 140rpm, slowing momentarily when the dodgems' load came on, then rapidly picking up, but not racing, their Pickering governors holding the reins, as clicks from relaxing piston rings bore witness, they were indeed lords of creation, noble and haughty. Lesser nhps would be going faster, the little 5s up to 180 or so and sometimes there would be a tiny steam tractor chipping away in a corner at 250 and more, generating lights for a side booth. Their flywheels would be revolving away from the threshing direction—as did a right-hand ploughing engine's—with a short belt, it being better to have the pull on the lower part, so that the dip on the top gave greater coverage on flywheel and dynamo pulley. Threeshaft engines would have their lever forward and links down; fourshafts had the lever back in reverse and links up. (This is less of a puzzle once it is realised that if the eccentric rods are changed over, and engine will turn in an opposite direction, with the link motion in the same place it was previously. As 'links down and lever forward' was an accepted arrangement for going forward, this was

65

the position with both types, even though the threeshaft's flywheel
went the same way as the road wheel, and, because of the extra
countershaft, the fourshaft's flywheel went the opposite way.)

The drivers had little to do but fire-up and wipe a rag over here
and there, and the fair-ground hands helped in polishing up before
a show. There was nothing like the extra work that went with a
threshing machine and no dust blowing about—a 'Bobbie's job' it
seemed. There was seldom occasion to get off the hard ground and
nearly always another engine for roping out when the wheels span,
and sunk in, and so little need for spudding—which would have
been frowned on anyway, their sort of ground being mostly local
authority's who did not welcome deep ruts. And they had the
effective road-engine brakes, which could be used instead of a block,
when changing gear. What with these and the compound's greater
holding capacity, there would be little concern about going down the
steepest hill, especially if there was a geared down pump, ideal on
the road, as it kept the water level just about right most of the time,
without pulling the steam about in the same way an injector could—
although, of course, these engines had injectors too.*

Was it because of these luxuries the drivers seemed to lack the
soldierly stance of the steam ploughman or the catlike gait that often
went with threshing? Mostly they were journeymen, who liked a
roving life. Agricultural men in work seldom wanted to be away from
home; and steam ploughmen, with Monday to Friday of van living
could not be kept away from it at week ends.

Thus members of the Showman's Guild had their share of difficulties. Those in a larger way liked to employ a maker's demonstration
man if they could tempt him to stop on for a time after the delivery
of a new engine, who would then, like the steam-plough foreman,
keep his eye on more than one engine, and teach likely youngsters.
And some of the stall owners—dominating men with great will power
and capacity—would, under his guidance, help-out by driving an
engine on the road, with a youngster steering. A few had even
attended what went, in those days, for a works' course. But this was
not sufficient compensation for the lack of a proper upbringing, and
the love it engendered; add to this the periods of insufficient sleep
and haphazard meals and the answer is spelt out in an engine's
sharpened pinion teeth and sloppy motion.

Those using the path between engines and pub, would, if it was

---

* Perhaps the rough times these drivers had and immense journeys they did between fairs
were sometimes overlooked.

on higher ground, be able to hear the varied exhausts and pick out from the smoke trails and occasional blowings-off midst the dazzling lights from where they came. Not all were so nicely modulated as the 'big ten'. There were plaintive wheezes and asthmatical sounds as well, blurring what would once have been clear 'chuffs', and with the steam tractor panting away in its corner like a large black dog.

Road Locomotives

These were showmen out-of-uniform. Sometimes they would change places. The road loco's awning seldom reached the chimney and only a few had governors, with some taking their pump-drive from the first countershaft (i.e. on a fourshaft), which necessitated using an injector when on belt work (but this seemed of little inconvenience when on the fairground).

The type began as ordinary threshing engines, generally 8nhp singles, hauling road-stone and timber between seasons. Some were steam-roller conversions, hauling in the summer and going back to rolling in the winter, where the smokebox and front axle assembly came off and was replaced by a roller's smokebox and fork, with the rear wheels replaced with smooth rolls. As soon as compounding came in, road locos were generally ordered as compounds, and a third speed, springs and extra water tanks followed in natural sequence. The military also became interested in them and developed their own specifications, which encouraged some makers to redesign models as road locomotives rather than build the extras into ordinary tractions. There was little difference in appearance, a greater boiler capacity being the chief feature.

When steam tractors and wagons came in, the use of heavy engines for general haulage declined. Some went threshing, but were only popular in districts where there was a good proportion of hard standing: they certainly made less fuss when the chaff-cutter was behind. Others were used on two-wagon timber haulage, and delivering special equipment, like large boilers and generators, when a front-mounted crane was found useful. Latterly, solid rubber tyres became standard, either with rings over the slats or delivered new with them. They increased adhesion and augmented the springs, and provided soft ground was avoided, were a great improvement. Timber engines were often supplemented by another engine iron shod, which could be spudded for working in the woods; or had their rubbers fitted crossways in angled segments. Spuds could then go on top, but were rarely needed, the rubberised slats being deep, with plenty of bite.

General-hauling like other branches of engine work often ran in families. It generated less engine-enthusiasm than threshing and ploughing; there was too much of the footplate and not enough time spent in walking round giving those little attentions which engines love to have and to which they respond so well. Timbering suited the countyman best and full use could be made of experience here, where extra lengths of wire rope came into play and pulley blocks were chained to trees for changes in direction. Rounds were rolled up the skids by putting the rope over the top and hooking to a couple of chains from underneath, their other ends fastened fore and aft to the timber drug. Then the watching driver had to be very quick with his lever for a dead stop should a mate raise his hand for a vital chain adjustment or forestalling the log's rolling over and off the cart; strangely shaped lengths in certain positions could do some unexpected things.

Knowing the road well was of immense help, and this could only come by repeated journeys over it. Then, when and where to fire-up and how much to put on, and when not to fire-up; how to have the water level just right for the gradients ahead; how to resist the temptation to use third wheel (top gear)—this better kept for level ground or running back empty—would come by instinct, and a reputation be building up with it.

It was not-knowing-the-road when troubles came. The new driver, or the old one on new ground were often prone to bad luck. Engines would run away down hills; find the softest place in a road and sink in; go over bridge parapets; and have trouble on tram lines. Also, with no time spent on belt work, there was a wearing-all-over and a tendency to break-downs. A front wheel would come off; a driving pin sheer; a back axle break; pinion teeth wear and snap and fusible plugs not only leak but blow right out. It was commonplace to see a heavy haulage engine temporarily abandoned on the grass verge, and not an out of the way phenomenon for it to be dangerously leaning over on one side, with a small crowd around. In addition, while the public remained 'horse-minded', owners faced persecution from police and road authorities. Thus were the business risks and overheads rather on the heavy side.

Steam Tractors

These were toy road locomotives for lesser tasks like furniture removing and hauling market garden produce. They came under a regulation for Light Locomotives (*see notes p.* 75) and were at first so restricted in weight that difficulties arose, especially with the single cylinder ones which were underboilered and underpowered; and all suffered from not enough adhesion until solid rubbers came in. As with their larger brothers, designers adopted compound cylinders as soon as they could, with a very great improvement in performance. Increases in efficiency stand out in greater prominence when there are limitations in size.

Two changes in the law benefited them. The first, in the early 1900s allowed an increase in weight to 5-tons. A few manufacturers produced a heavier tractor then, which had a wider appeal, when some were used at threshing and on the fairgrounds, not too heavy belt work being within their scope if the steam pressure was kept well up. The second change, in the 1920s, came too late to save them from extinction, although three makers re-designed to take advantage of the greater weight ceiling.

A job even the lighter compounds were good at, was timber hauling. They could 'snig' and load as well as a big engine, were more manoeuvrable, and could go where others feared to tread. There would only be one timber wagon behind; but on relatively short hauls this did not matter so much, their speed being compensation.

A driver new to tractors took time to accustom himself to the small amount of room, especially a steam ploughman, who was likely to burn himself every time he leaned down to fire-up, with such close packed pipes and taps, in spite of the asbestos string wrapped round wherever it would go (and which had a habit, like a boy's first bootlace, in often coming undone).

One had to be a contortionist to fire-up when travelling. A way was to fill the shovel from the top of the bunker, bend down, and aim at the fire from between the legs. There was usually no opening to the footplate and the steersman sat with his feet straddling the side plate, well back over the bunker. Some drivers were wont to sit side-saddle on a rolled sack over the reverse lever slides: a practice derided by the older men, who held that one could never drive an engine properly, sitting down. In a way they were right, particularly before mechanical lubricators came in, when a very close eye would always be cast forward on valve and piston rods for the tell-tale signs of the displacement lubricators' running out—which were of strangely small capacity. It was dangerous to leave a steam tractor for long, especially when blowing off, as the water would go down the glass with unexpected rapidity, and not always could the tiny injector be persuaded to start then, which meant a quick fall-back on the geared-down pump, often after a block-up and out-of-gear whizz-round. Keeping the steam pressure high was the thing. Any lowering, and the power would be gone. Thus did tubes have to be swept and firebars clean, and drivers were always seen 'poking about at something'.

Overtype Steam Wagons

A man only used to traction engines having his first ride on a steam wagon could find it 'an alarming experience as there was up to four times the speed and little notice taken of hills.

However, even if the methods of driving were so different, keeping steam was much the same, and a learner would be inside, doing just this, while the driver sat behind the flywheel steering with one hand and regulating with the other. The driver would also keep his eye on the water level shown in a sloping glass, faced towards him. If the slow-running pump were friction driven, rather at about a 3 : 1 ratio, this would be working most of the time and supplemented by the injector when it could not keep-up. The injector, straight off the boiler end, worked better than most and needed little or no adjustment with the water tap. Perhaps a reason was that the tank was far back, slung beneath the chassis and out of reach of coal particles. For a run down hill and no steam being taken, the pump was pulled away from its friction drive by tipping the upwards pressing spring-loading downwards by the half-turn of a handled eccentric. Pumps on later models were driven by a fine-mesh chain, and were thus always on, and their water supply regulated by a tap. These did not return unused water like the traction's pump, but were reliable enough providing there were no leaks in the suction pipe. Not all mates wanted to be drivers, however, when, with the older chain steered wagons, these would then be outside steering with the driver inside, regulating and keeping steam. This method was discarded when Ackerman steering came in, together with three speeds, making it essential for the driver to be in control of speed and direction.

The steam wagon gear arrangements resembled a threeshaft traction's and a long chain went to the back axle from the single countershaft, the sprocket there containing the differentials.

The regulator was straight across, push-to-open and shutting back on a pin. If the pin was pulled out and put in on the other side of the regulator, it could be pull-to-open, when, instead of compounding, high pressure steam would go into the low pressure cylinder—similarly to when the 'compound button' was pressed on a traction. Here, however, 'double-high' was often needed for more than just a start or overcoming a short peak demand, when, to avoid exhaust back-pressure, a straight in-and-out lever was pulled to open a separate exhaust from the high pressure cylinder to the chimney. Then the exhaust-beat clearly changed from two-to-a-rev to four, 'like a train'. Care had to be taken with its use, as hard pulling for long would draw too much cold air into the firebox. When shunting, it was easier if double-high were used, but with a gentle hand. Later wagons had a trigger replacing the pin. Had this and a few other improvements not been done it is likely that a line of father to son drivers would have eventually developed a third arm, changes of limb or fin often being nature's answer to environmental demands.

The reverse lever—close to the driver's regulator hand—would not be used for braking lest it make the chain judder. There was an effective foot brake which could be left on with a ratchet, and a screw-on hand brake in addition, and sometimes the frowned-on flywheel brake too.

Models with chain steering had this higher geared than a traction's and with a small wheel for quicker turning. The later Ackerman steering had a large wheel which needed little moving by comparison. Wagons were good steamers, their short thick boilers keeping up with most demands on them and the water-level less affected by gradients; yet a little blowing-off would soon pull the water down.

Undertype Wagons

These seemed made especially to do without a proper engineman, requiring few of the skills he had acquired. The engine had two high pressure cylinders, poppet valves and was underneath, enclosed and self-oiling. The upright boiler did not have its water-level influenced by hills. Even so, having charge was all the easier for one who understood steam. A dry firebox top was still to be feared and this type too could suffer from priming. Later developments were a higher pressure boiler behind the driver and an open ended engine (needing no packing) with four cylinders set across the frame shaft-driving the back axle. When these came in the overtype was out of date, being too slow and requiring too much attention from its driver (which left several overtype makers in mid air, as it were, with some belatedly experimenting with advanced undertypes). Then came—in the early thirties what is generally regarded as the death blow to road haulage by steam, in the form of excessive taxation—with show-men and agricultural engines exempted. Without this, however, it is still doubtful if steam could have withstood competition from the increasingly reliable diesel engine; steam, that is, as it has been known. It is hard to imagine a steam plant developing as much power for the same weight as a diesel engine and requiring no more training, attention and skill, unless indeed the pollution which internal combustion engines are building up in the atmosphere forces enough research to achieve it.

Undertype wagons—but only a few—were the first in the field, with various designs of upright boiler as well as the horizontal loco-motive type and one straight across with the firebox in the middle. But as long as they had the conventional compound engine with slide valves and link motion reverse they were not successful. Com-pounds require dry steam, which they could not get, slung down below, well away from the boiler, and were especially troublesome when starting from cold. But as soon as the compound was placed on top of the boiler, on the lines of a traction engine, its success was assured; hence the overtype. But this 'reliability at any price', with a poor power-to-weight ratio and too much room taken up in front was half-a-step-backwards, and delayed development. Firms who had faith in the undertype persevered, replacing the compound engine with one having two high-pressure cylinders and getting dryer steam by superheating. The superheater was a copper coil in the smokebox which could be easily steam-hosed down, to clear it from accumulating soot, by a flexible metal pipe. Boilers had increased pressure and remained upright, with a firing tube going through from the top to a deep firebox, with short vertical or sloping tubes.

Steam Rollers

These were never glamorous and their early drivers learned on the job, and seldom had every nerve a-tremble with the ancillary worries of other men, like what might be happening at the other end of a field or behind a threshing machine. All they were required to do was amble their roller backwards and forwards, periodically stopping to fire-up or draw-in water. Thus when engines were in general use, rollers did not attract the more adventurous nor those anxious for fame.

A desire for fame, mixed with a little vanity, was what sustained many in the poorly paid agricultural world, where an experienced man could become known and revered over a wide area. Necessity developing his invention, he could turn his hand to anything; weighing up and dealing with changing situations gave him an air of authority; moving around the farms could result in pleasant anecdotes and wise sayings and the getting up of steam made him a man of early mornings. These were the sort who came onto the rolling scene in later days when there was no other engine-work for them to do, as it had so happened that not long after a famous statesman said that the lights of Europe were going out one by one, the fires of engines began to go out one by one too.

Steam ploughs were the first to go, and soon there was only a nucleus for pond and river dredging. The Fordson tractor started this trend when demonstrated in World War I as a manpower saver, compared well with the five-man steam plough team, even if it could not do such heavy work. The tractor also had its effect on the threshing engine, as when fitted with a belt pulley it first began to displace farmer-owned portables. It next ate into the threshing contractor's preserve when farmers who owned tractors would sometimes go-in for a threshing machine too. This met with varying success because few understood threshers, and moving one about the farm was difficult, because of the tractor's lack of adhesion. However, as soon as pneumatic tyres came in for tractors and it was found they could be fitted with a winch and anchor there was no trouble in getting a drum anywhere on the farm and the weight of this added to the tyres' adhesion made them safe for hauling the tackle on the road as well. When then compared with the traction engine there was greater manoeuvrability, less cost in fuel and less skill required. Thus did threshing contractors begin to change over to tractors too, aided by the fact that many engine drivers, regrettably, had regarded themselves as indispensable, with a few developing temperaments, the which could not be suffered in competitive times.

Fair-ground engines were gradually stood off when they required heavy repair, in favour of diesel power, which did not need a man to be in attendance at the generating point. Sometimes this was a separate plant mounted on a lorry, and it was also found that for lighter work the lorry engine itself could drive the generator.

Timber hauliers began to use specially designed four-wheeled drive tractors, both petrol and diesel with powerful winches, which were better than steam on soft ground and also faster on the road.

Users of steam wagons, with very few exceptions, had changed to petrol and diesel by the middle thirties, stimulated by the prohibitive tax although there were concessions for showmen and those used in road repair, as when fitted with tanks for steam-heating and spraying tar.

Thus was the humble steam roller the last refuge of many who had had a proper engine upbringing and who could thresh-and-cut and splice a wire-rope as well as any. These men showed up well on hired rollers, which often had to travel long distances between sites with van and water-cart. Getting them about, single handed was no mean task. A 'very great deal' would go on at a single firing, then she'd go four or five miles without a stop, the non-steering hand frequently adjusting the ashpan-lid and now and then going to the steam tap on the injector after an almost always lucky setting of the water tap, checked for dribbles by a quick glance behind. And going down hills was no trouble either, the lever drawn back beyond centre to the first notch the other side if a steep one, and should there be too much slowing up, a short spell in the centre or a forward notch would soon regain speed. The most difficult types were the earlier ones where the regulator rod did not come through the steam chest at the far end. It proved better to have a blowing gland there than a blank end, as, when holding with the lever, immediately the centre point was past, the regulator would snap open, causing much jerking, and to the uninitiated, a risk of things getting out-of-hand. In such cases the regulator had to be held shut with the steering hand and the wheel leaned against in an attempt to hold a straight course. If the hill was long and steep, these rollers would be better changed down to low gear.

The life could be pleasant enough, the van being no hardship for the ex-steam ploughman, and some were able to persuade their wives to share it with them, which meant an end to scrounging for food, and lone uncoiling of the water pipe; and blocking up for a gear-change was then, of course, dead easy. Even if there was no governor to help with a rhythm, there was still a regulator, a reverse lever and a geared-down steering wheel to remind them of the reality of things! But rollers were a come-down really, when you looked back to the time of being in charge of a pair of large and magnificent ploughing engines, even if they were an escape from a winter's threshing dust.

In the end, however, despite some manufacturers' valiant efforts to keep steam in being by improved weight distribution and wider wheels for the newer road materials, steam rollers too were stood off one by one. Raising steam after a standing period on the roadside began to look a time-consuming process—with no straw to start the fire and seldom dry wood handy either. Then diesels were smoother starting, unless the steamer was very carefully handled; a jerky start would hollow-out wheel marks on a black-top surface. Also they could be handled by any lorry driver should the roller man be absent. So, like the showmen, steam rollers were not put back into serve whenever a heavy repair became due.

The advent of reliable diesel power was a boon to those who had never driven anything but rollers, being both easier and cleaner; but a sad day for the real engineman. He never got quite used to the long boring hours of just sitting, easing a clutch lever forward and back and holding a wheel like a car's. Far better had it been to stand, fully in command, with a low-geared wheel to turn, proper levers to push and pull with careful timings, and the shovelling, oiling, tapping, adjusting, tightening and all the little things to do to make an engine appreciative and return your affection, by turning over quietly with a little sibilance and smiling at you through its smoke.

A list—Acts, Regulations & Orders

Locomotives on Highways Act, 1896

This defined a motor or light locomotive as a vehicle weighing under 3-tons unladen and not used to draw more than one vehicle.

The combination being limited to 4-tons unladen

Locomotives Act, 1898

This was the outcome of evidence given before the select committee. It qualified certain provisions in the Act of 1896 regarding hours of travelling.

Motor Car Act, 1903

Local Government Boards given the power to regular the speed of motor cars exceeding 2-tons unladen. Late in 1904 this board increased the max. weight of a heavy motor car to 5-tons unladen and if drawing a trailer, to 6½ tons with the trailer. Speeds were limited to 5, 8 and 12mph according to weight. This was known as:

The Heavy Motor Car Order, 1904

This applied only to England and Wales. Similar regulations were made early in 1905 to apply to Ireland and Scotland.

The system of registration and identification of light locomotives set up under the '*Motor Car Act of* 1903'—continued until the end of 1920.

In 1910 the additional 'carriage duty' charged on light locomotives was removed and a scale of duties for motor cars was issued, this being based on horsepower.

Finance Act, 1920

Concessions were made in respect of agricultural engines and tractors.

Road Vehicles (Registration and Licensing Regulations, 1924)

These limited the weight of locomotives to 15½ tons, which could be exceeded in certain cases, for instance, where a permanent crane or winding drum was carried, also where the wheels had pneumatic or 'soft' tyres.

The Heavy Motor Car (Amendment) Order, 1927

This dealt with such matters as overhang, max. length, braking and included the much-discussed point that a vehicle with three axles could have a length of up to 30ft. Ground clearance also received consideration.

9 Which were the Best Engines?

This would have been a risky question when there were plenty of drivers about and often would have been the answer 'mine'. Partisan feeling was strong and some only knew one engine all their lives with a son sometimes following them on it. With any engine in good order it would not have been a bad reply, as there were no really bad engines only some which were better than others. Makes varied and so did examples of the same make. All were made by craftsmen, and few differed more than marginally in construction and finish, with their owners and drivers close in outlook, as performance was in their mutual interest.

Their were divergencies, however, in the threshing trade, which was the biggest user. Where there was not much soft ground a driver would prefer a large engine because it could go for longer periods between firings and shunt about more gently and on lower steam. But the farmer thought a large engine used more coal—which he had to find—and might do more damage to his rickyard with its weight. Thus did an owner tend to go his customer's way as far as he could. But too small an engine would not handle the tackle on the road safely, and had to have a constant eye kept on it when threshing, which, on a busy day when the driver was wanted everywhere at once was a drawback. And on the not such busy days too, an engine which could be left for a while for a little gossip over the gate was thought the better-of. So if an owner had a choice—not all did, some inheriting engines—it usually fell on a 7nhp single. A compound could be a nhp less for the same weight and power, but its higher capital cost was hardly worth-while for the great proportion of light work it did, fuel economy only showing up when threshing-and-cutting, or when there was hauling as well as belt work. Also there was twice as much motion cleaning and oiling to do and the tubes had to be swept more often.

With ploughing engines compounds were the thing as soon as they became available, towards the end of the last century. Few then ordered new singles although many of these were kept in being by small firms who modified them to tandem, (end to end) or 'single crank', compounds (which will be described later), or rebuilt the top-work, substituting piston valves. A single was often working to the limit of its capacity, when it could then be clearly seen that the excessive blast from the chimney was a waste of power and that it would be better to harness some of this to move a second piston-block. The slightest lapse from A1 condition and it could burn coal at a phenomenal rate and often be waiting for the water-cart, with the longer-term effects of burning out chimney and smokebox plating. Replacement smokeboxes were generally enlarged, extending beyond the chimney, which cut down the rapid wear as the blast was then partly equalised, and it gave a more 'powerful' appearance too; yet this was only a palliative.

It took time for owners to realise, when they bought compounds, that the larger they were the better, within limits, as although more fuel per hour might be used there was less per acre, and their larger implements needed no more men. The '16nhp' size dubbed by Fowlerss 'BBs', and later, 'BB 1s', was deemed the optimum. The next size up, '18s' or 'AAs' were rather wide for most gateways. Larger sizes than these were rarely seen in this country, as to spread their weight over the headlands their wheels had to be broader still. Larger engines could also carry a greater length of rope, some up to 800yd, where the 8 and 10nhp compounds had 450 or so, which meant tackling big fields in two sections. When compounds became general the three main ploughing engine makers had no more competition from others.

Road engines too were preferred as compounds, being then quieter, travelling further on a tank of water and needing less changing-down on hills. The showman's 10nhp was only popular when the belt-work was heavy and fluctuating; 8nhps were the favoured size for most types of work, nearly all makers offered a Road Loco, yet two firms monopolised the orders, only losing them to others when their delivery dates were too far ahead.

In the heyday of the traction engine there were eighteen manufacturers regularly producing them. Those from the larger firms were seen all over the country, while the smaller ones tended to be grouped around their places of origin. The former, having a good export trade developed a good spares service, supplying parts which would fit with little or no alteration; while the latter had to convince customers, that because they were close, they could give personal service, sending fitters out to do the job—where so often a part which looked right would not go on without further skilled shaping on the site.

These makers were:

William Allchin, Globe Works, Northampton
Aveling & Porter, Rochester
Charles Burrell & Sons, St. Nicholas Works, Thetford
Clayton & Shuttleworth, Stamp End Works, Lincoln
William Foden, Elworth Works, Sandbach
William Foster, Wellington Foundry, Lincoln
Fowell & Co, St Ives
John Fowler & Co, Steam Plough Works, Leeds
Richard Garrett, Leiston
Richard Hornsby, Spittlegate Iron Works, Grantham
J. & H. McLaren, Midland Engine Works, Leeds
Marshall, Sons & Co, Britannia Works, Gainsborough
Mann's Steam Cart & Wagon Co, Hunslet, Leeds
Ransomes, Sims & Jefferies, Orwell Works, Ipswich
Robey & Co, Globe Works, Lincoln
Ruston & Proctor, Sheet Iron Works, Lincoln
William Tasker, Andover
Wallis & Steevens, Basingstoke

The era before the turn of the century was a threeshaft one, excepting a very early Clayton model; ploughing engines; Aveling & Porter rollers since 1871 and the Foden traction engine (which came late in the day). At various times around 1900 there came a change to fourshafts, with the exception of Burrells, Wallis & Steevens and Fowell, which remained threeshafts. It is not clear why this change was made. It could be because the fourshaft is narrower, and easier for gateways, which was what William Fletcher, the designer who first showed his influence with Claytons, always tried to achieve; and also, of course, to give more room for bearings, his big-end being particularly massive, and so lasting longer between adjustments. His first effort however, followed the above mentioned fourshaft not of his design, very old-fashioned and with front-mass steerage, was a long boilered threeshaft with the safety-valves on the boiler barrel between the steam-chest and chimney and front wheels set back, to give a shorter turning lock. However, this was soon replaced by his well known and handsome fourshaft with the pump eccentric outside the hornplate and pump alongside the boiler, like a portable's. These two features narrowed the track by half the width of the threeshaft's countershaft (because of the two speeds on it) and some of the width of the pump eccentric. With the two-speed gears now inside the hornplate on an extra shaft, the large pinion on what was now the second countershaft was only a single one instead of being doubled. Fletcher slid these second shaft's pinions in and out of gear by an upright handle not unlike a locomotive's regulator handle placed immediately in front of the driver, while other designers had their change-speed lever well over to the off-side in a horizontal position, sometimes with the end turned up, handle-wise, when the regulator was like this too. (Fletcher also designed the later Ransomes, and Davy-Paxman engines which were in many ways similar. Avelings had their pumps outside too.)

Another reason for the change to fourshafts may have been the extra weight of the threeshaft's overhanging gears, just outside the bearing which takes most of the crank's thrust, increasing an already unequal wear there. Then there could have been a greater cost in making threeshaft gears, with one drive pinion sliding inside another. Also drivers mostly favoured fourshafts. Some said there was a risk, with a threeshaft's forward running flywheel, of a stone being thrown up into the steersman's face (by coincidence all threeshafts, except Richard Hornsby's steered on the flywheel side). Others that when new there was insufficient play in the gearing—with only one inter-mediate set of them—to hand-pull the flywheel off a dead centre. There was also a view that engines with short connections are smoother at higher revs. Certainly the threeshaft had the longer con-necting rod, where something could be said for counterbalancing its extra weight—which is what Burrells did in their later singles and single-crank compounds, where previously only double-crank com-pounds had been balanced.

Changes in appearance were few after 1900. Claytons slimmed the Fletcher engine; Allchins, later, offered a new threeshaft 'as an alternative' and said it would pull more on the road than an equal fourshaft. Marshalls tried a piston valve—which never caught on; Fowler boilers got larger, and Aveling's smaller—the latter also trying piston valves for a while; Fosters altered their outline; and Pickering governors became more popular.

Fowlers were the first in the field with a compound, using the double-crank principle with connecting rods outside the link-motions, which were slanted to move valves on top of the steam chest. The cranks were then close to the bearings and the steam came in

Top: Early 3-shaft of about 1887. Owner Mr. T. T. Boughton (with bowler) standing alongside, 1899. Machine at end of the drum is a straw-tyer.

Above: Later type Fowler, a 4-shaft. This 8nhp single *(Black Jack)* was purchased new by Mr Boughton soon after the above was taken, and is here seen threshing some forty years later.

Facing page.
Top: Threshing and Cutting. Chaff being bagged off. Blowing
through piping into the barn took more power and was stimulated by
a shortage of farm men. */J. P. Mullett*

Centre: Threshing and Baling with *Black Jack*. The baler was much
easier to drive than a chaff-cutter, but rarely seen behind a drum
until the late 1930s. */J. P. Mullett*

Foot: Fowler 7nhp single. */T. T. Boughton & Sons Ltd.*

Below: Wallis and Steevens, Threshing. The reverse lever is back and
links up here, as on all threeshaft engines when threshing, although
some drivers liked to cross the belt to avoid this. */J. P. Mullett*

Foot: Fowler *Black Jack*

Facing page.
Top: 7nhp Allchin No 1105 (FP 1024). /*A. J. Martin*

Centre: Clayton and Shuttleworth (Post Fletcher). /*A. J. Martin*

Foot: C. E. Kimbell's 7nhp Foster No 14423 at Boughton, Northants in 1924. Driver Richard Leak now 82 and mate George Brown now 73, the youth is the author.

Top: Fowell at Penshunt Rally, Kent. /*J. H. Meredith*

Above: Gordon Lugg and son on Foster *The Little Gem* No 14638 (VL 4777) 5nhp built in 1933. Marshall No 84562 (KP 6969) in rear. /*A. J. Martin*

Top: Engine on left is Ruston & Hornsby No 113043 (CE 7977) built 1920 and engine on right is Ruston Proctor No 50278 (CE 7949) built 1914. /*J. H. Meredith*

Above: Marshall No 84562 (KP 6969) built in 1929. /*A. J. Martin*

Top: 7nhp Marshall No 83780 (VF 4183) built in 1928. /*A. J. Martin*

Above: Robey No 28094 (AO 8932) 5hp built in 1908. /*A.J. Martin*

Top: Wallis and Steevens No 7293 *Pandora.* /*A. J. Martin*

Above: Early Fowler single, rebuilt as a compound. Only four of these
were made. /*J. H. Meredith*

Top: Early Fowler No 2692, (new 1886) 12nhp at Rempstone, Leics.
Reboilered by John Allen's (Oxford) with John Allen cast iron chimney.
/A. J. Martin

Above: J. Orchard's Fowler No 2623 *Papworth* 12nhp built in 1875.
/Road Locomotive Society

Facing page.

Top: Fowler BB1 No 15203 (BH 7344). /*A. J. Martin*

Centre: Compound ploughing engine by Aveling and Porter RH No 7445
King George V (KR 4257). /*F. G. I. Stokes*

Foot: A. T. Oliver's 16nhp McLaren No 1551 (NK 933) built in 1918.
/*A. J. Martin*

Below: Fowler No 16264 class B6 8nhp. /*Road Locomotive Society*

Foot: Foden D-type tractor No 13802 (UN 2912) and Foden trailer.
/*A. J. Martin*

Top: Burrell tractor No 3458 *Defiance* (AB 8795) built in 1913. /*A. J. Martin*

Above: Early Tasker compound. Later ones had outside valves. /*A. J. Martin*

Facing page.
Top: Garrett No 33219 (BJ 6180) built in 1918. /*A. J. Martin*

Centre: 6-ton Foden No 11012 (MO 1552) and Foden trailer. /*A. J. Martin*

Foot: Foden No 2022 *Perseverance* (M 2519) built in 1910. /*A. J. Martin*

Facing page.
Top: Bradford Corporation's 5-ton Clayton and Shuttleworth tipper No 47762 (FE 2162). /*A. J. Martin*

Centre: 5-ton Allchin No 1261 (NH 976) built in 1922. /*A. J. Martin*

Foot: Sentinel DG6 No 8604 *Margaret* (JF 2022). /*A. J. Martin*

Below: H. Bonnett's Fowler compound No 17077 taking water from the River Wye. /*A. J. Martin*

Foot: Wallis and Steevens No 7785. /*J. H. Meredith*

Top: Aveling and Porter No 12450 (PG 1711). /*S. Clennell*

Above: P. Collins's Burrell Showman *The Griffin* No 2804 (DH 2542) 8nhp built in 1906.

from the top, where it was driest: both ideal arrangements. Compounds made by Marshall, Foster and Robey followed this example. Ransomes, Burrells and McLarens had the valves outside the steam chest, where the links were then outside and the cranks away from their bearings, less desirable theoretically, although no harm came of it, but larger compounds of this type had an extra bearing between the cranks. Wallis & Steevens, Aveling & Porter, Ruston-Proctor and Tasker (Tractors) also began with the Fowler arrangement, then changed to valves-on-the-sides (pistons when they became Ruston-Hornsby) possibly because of ease of manufacture, and certainly this way was better for maintenance and adjustment. Claytons also changed over to side valves, but with different drive designs, and Allchins had them either way, the customer always being more right with them than he was with any other firm. On the question of compound crank balancing, most makers put split balance weights on each; Marshalls and Avelings did without them for quite a long time; and McLarens had a single weight between the close-together cranks, as was the practice with most steam wagons, which all ended up with outside valves.

Ploughing engines made by Fowler and by Aveling had left-hand steering, and compound only ploughing engines by McLaren, right-hand steering. Traction engines by Fowler, Marshall, Aveling and Allchin had right-hand steering. All the other makers favoured left-hand steering, Allchin again ringing the changes, but with a left-hand tendency after 1914, and Fowler making their last few road locos with left-hand steering. All steam tractors except McLaren's and Ruston's were threeshaft, this saved weight, a big factor, and doubtless, as they were narrow enough already, they could afford it! And all except McLaren's steered from the left. Most steam rollers except the lighter ones on the steam tractor plan, and Wallis & Steevens', had right-hand steering. Burrells, Fowlers and Allchins (again) stepped out of pattern here with steering 'on the other side' when required. Then, as in most forms of creation, either direct from nature or via man, there were rogue types: lapses from orthodoxy after a trend had been set and before its discarding. Thus did one sometimes see the unbelievable, such as fourshaft Burrells (limited to rollers); valves-on-top Ransomes; right-hand steered Claytons and left-hand steered Marshalls (their tractors, of course, were always left-hand).

10 Surveying the Makes

William Allchin

This firm was founded in the middle of the last century and went into voluntary liquidation in 1931. Going round their works at that time one might be forgiven for imagining the date was 30 years earlier with the machine-shop having the oldest of belt driven tools and the boiler-shop only needing a few horseshoes on hooks to resemble a blacksmiths. There was a Lancashire boiler, and stationary engine with expansion-gear (where the governor coupled onto a second slide-valve outside the main one, shortening the travel of this, as an alternative to a throttling-valve) to drive the machinery. This was stood-off about a year before the end and its place taken by compound steam roller, which had been long in stock. This was backed up to the line-shafting and fitted with governors, a tin roofed shed, and an extension to the chimney going through. The addition was from a very old Aveling & Porter single cylindered road engine which had long stood rusting in the yard after having been part-exchanged for a new wagon in Sheffield.

Great advances have, of course, been made in the engineering world since that time, but even then, batch production and an attempt at standardising parts was in vogue. However, if speed and cost of production are not stressed, it can be said that the fewer aids in a workshop the greater the skill of the men. Allchin's were certainly as good as could be found anywhere and apprentices trained with them have since done well in many spheres.

From 1912 the firm was chiefly noted for its steam wagon. Previously the engine had been tried underneath the chassis. Not being successful here it was then placed on top of the horizontal boiler, traction engine-wise, at first with the valves on top of the steam chest, before going on to the sides, as was usual with steam wagons. For a time they were a success, sold well and in the middle twenties began to have Ackerman steering and three-speeds. Yet their working pressure remained at 200lb where rivals had 20lb more; nor had research gone into valve lengths and travel. Thus they were sluggish when comparisons were made.

Allchins were possibly the first portable engine makers to provide a bored cylindrical guide for the crosshead to run in, where others began with two pairs of parallel bars between which its recessed edges ran. To diverse, this certainly did not pander to the Victorian idea of massiveness, as, viewed from the side the block appeared flimsy: little more than an elbowed joint. Better looking were the differing patterns of crosshead set vertically between single top and bottom bars, as used by Fowlers and Burrells. But most makers changed to the cylindrical guide, except Wallis & Steevens and Ransomes, and even some of the latter had them, with Fowlers going over to them too in their latest rollers. Crosshead shapes within the cylindrical guide and the amount they were concealed also varied with make. The more they were hidden the more they seemed to gain in attraction—as do some other things in life—and this type were more efficient too, with no risk of losing alignment, and retaining their lubrication better. The recesses at either ends of the slide were always full of oil, which seeped from the crosshead pin, this fed from the upper slide's lickings from a siphon wool out of the brass capped cup on top. There were holes underneath, generally bunged by cork. The cylinder end recess was rarely drained, as, splashing up when it met the sliding block, the oil went on to the piston rod as it plunged in and out of its gland alleviating the wet running, when there was too much water in or not enough steam pressure.

Thus did it come about that the very first Allchin traction engines had cylindrical crosshead guides. Lacking a Fletcher, they may have been over-broad, but their shortness was some compensation, and to achieve it the guide was nearer the crankshaft than on any other, resulting in a shorter and less unbalanced connecting rod which, with valve-rods and governor belt, ran through slots and eyepieces in a most concealing spectacle-plate, so that only the driver looking down at it could see the crank pin in its nakedness. One might have expected a large Burrell-like space then, between chimney base and cylinder head. But this was avoided with no loss of boiler volume, a slightly greater girth compensating. There was no need then to have the ugly (in a traction, but less so with a wagon) set-back front axle to achieve a short turn, and afterwards having to discard it because of complaints of front-lifting; as did some others: Allchins rarely reared. A further good point was making a trailer follow-myleader by plenty of rear overhang, which also gave a large tank and bunker. Thus would a threshing machine less often have to be uncoupled and shunted or chained through a gateway than with a longer wheel based engine. Also from the first the push-regulator was easy moving, the response gentle, reversing precise, steaming good and priming seldom seen.

The first threeshafts had right-hand steering and large ugly portable engine type governors, but were soon changed to the more familiar crossarms. The counter-shaft had separate high and low gear pinions on either side, the former on the near side between flywheel and bearing and each had its own gear lever. It was then possible to get both gears in at once—but one would think few drivers would do this many times and such an error took but little rectifying. Yet rival makers' catalogues were always stressing the impossibility of their models getting into this sort of fix by levers which interlocked or a single one which had differing fulcrums, so then, rather than design the less simple and more expensive both-gears-on-the-offside Allchin's sensitive directors plumbed for a fourshaft earlier than most, which just happened to be excellent, compact, neat with a nicely tapered chimney and well proportioned copper top.

But to go back to the early threeshaft the chief fault was the flywheel's overhang. It did not look right, so far away from its bearing and also caused the track to be broader to make room for it. Yet Fowlers had long overcome this difficulty with their ploughing engines, where the spokes were curved back after making room for the vertical-shaft bevel, so that the rim and most of the weight were near the bearing and room made for the rear wheel to come closer. Their Lion Road Locos also had a dished flywheel to make room for a similar outside-the-frame top gear pinion. However, this idea never occurred to Allchins, nor for that matter to any other threeshaft maker. Had they done so the course of history may have been different, with hardly a fourshaft seen, as it did not take long, when compounds were made, for their of-necessity far-apart crankshaft pinions—one inside the near bearing and the other outside the offside one, threeshaft-wise—to have varying forms of relationship which prevented them both being engaged at once.

The Allchin fourshaft had similar dimensions to the threeshaft, a little elongated and less stubby because of the extra shaft and in its usual 7nhp form with 5ft 10in instead of 5ft 8in wheels, the same 16in width. It still seemed remarkable that such a small unit should have a 12in stroke and the power and voice of a 7nhp. Rather 'empty' this was at first, shallow and not clean-cut. Then, at about the time when the perch under the smokebox was changed from a kind of pedestal to a broader fabricated bracket something was done inside which made a deeper sound, with a distinctive hollow big-drum-like thump when idling over slowly; nothing metallic but suggesting an echoing and slight sucking-back. It did not always happen and never when there was any more than the slightest whisp of steam on. Opened-up, it would now chuff clean. Those who remember Webb locomotives from the ex-London & North Western Railway will know—they chiffed rather than chuffed. A further alteration in 1909 was the name in set-out lettering around the top half of the smokebox door and 'Northampton' around the bottom, and which remained on all subsequent engines.

The crossarm governors were less sensitive and harder driving than most, so that when oil from the gear pinions got onto the belt this would slip unless kept rigidly tight, with sluggish pick-ups whenever a half-opened sheaf went down the drum, and heavy coal consumption resulted.

Thus around 1912 Pickering governors began to be seen, albeit, rather late in the day. These were driven from a countershaft to allow the belt to come out of the spectacle plate horizontally, as it had always done before, preserving the modesty of the things inside. To have slanted it, as was afterwards done on the redesigned three-shaft, would have meant a more revealing slot or its complete removal! Then was belt performance greatly improved, and as if to mark such an innovation the steering was removed to the left. This model just happened to be the best Allchin threshing engine of all.

Afterwards they became as heavy as any of their rivals with needless extra weight, culminating in the extended smokebox and larger wheels of Royal Chester, that most modelled of engines. Trying to be too much like the others caused a loss of identity. Sales were then getting difficult, so with one-off production the temptation to bend too much to customers' whims was hard to resist. Thus did three-shafts return, when required, but of orthodox pattern with the speeds on the off-side. So did right-hand steering, and tubes could be had with 1½in or 2in diameter, Gardener governors instead of Pickerings (upside down, as on Ransomes) and compounds with valves on top or on the sides were further alternatives.

Allchin directors were over impressed with what others thought, and lacking a designer with some backbone their models 'kind of evolved', and though the products were most successful when they were different from others, they yet followed the very human failing of trying to conform to a norm. This had its effect on spares, and even when two engines looked alike, a part from one would seldom fit the other without considerable filing and scraping. The firm treated this lightly, holding that few non-moving parts of their engines ever broke and that wearing one like piston rings and rods (where they passed through the gland) and bearings could easily be made in any small workshop, or alternatively they would send a man out with the basic parts to fit on site. This had its effect on sales, and few large owners wanted Allchins.

The half dozen single cylinder steam rollers they made were 6nhp tractions of the earlier fourshaft pattern with rollers on, and a distinctive design of their own to hold the front-piece comprising the fork and its stalk, which could move sideways as good as any other. But they had poor coverage on a bend and missed a piece in full lock. Only half a dozen were made, and as many compounds, four of which were threeshafts with outside valves (it was one of those which drove the shop for a time). These were even worse on a bend and tarmac would well-up in ridges between where the front wheel left off and the rear began. Unless steam was kept well up they were wet running, rumoured to be because the lp cylinder's diameter was too large in proportion to the hp's—yet this did not differ from Fowler diameters. Thus on demanding-work they were often blowing off, and as the Ramsbottom safety-valves were not of the best they rarely shut off properly. One owner overcame this fault by fitting a locomotive 'pop' type safety valve, which would blast off without warning and as quickly shut off again. He esteemed it a great improvement; but this would not have been allowed when horses were numerous on the roads.

Allchin rollers and the few 8nhp tractions on springs and with belly tanks, which the firm dubbed road locos, had filled-in flywheels; a disc in front of the spokes. Most other makes had genuine disc flywheels for other than agricultural engines, Marshall's being a pressing with the flat surface relieved by a ringed indenture at half the diameter. Discs were obligatory for engines which spent most of their time on the roads as spokes were thought to alarm horses, and spokes could have been more dangerous for getting-near-to when revolving slowly, although no accident here has been recorded.

Aveling & Porter

Thomas Aveling has been mentioned as making the first self-moving agricultural engine and extending the firebox outer-shell to hold the crankshaft. He also invented chain-and-roller steering so that the driver could steer too when he wanted.

Before then, portable engine type brackets held the crankshaft and a man sat in front, steering with a pilot wheel; and, when the crankshaft was over the firebox, chain-driving the back-axle via a countershaft bracketed to the side of the boiler (on an engine which appeared in 1861) the first traction in familiar guise had made its debut. An improvement soon followed, with the countershaft going full width so that two brackets shared its load. The steam roller was developed from this by having its wheels smooth and towing an enormous 'garden roller' some 10ft in diameter. The very great interest which this stimulated and its wider application than to anything in the agricultural field, gave rise to the desirability of a roller as an integral unit.

Here it seemed there was a loss of self-confidence, the first attempts being from an outside consulting engineer's ideas, because of previous experience in consolidating road materials. Weighing 30-tons it had Aveling top-work chain-driving the rear wheels in the above way, via countershaft and chain. But the axle was set forward, halfway along the boiler. A frame bent back from the axle ends past the driver's footplate to embrance an elongated turntable, with the steering roller in its lower half and a water tank on top. Because the tank moved round with the steering, part of the pump feed was by flexible hose, and the pump was on top of the boiler in-line with the crosshead guides. Steering had a likeness to the back-hand steam ploughing engine's, a sprocket on the end of a verticle-shaft having a chain reaching round the turntable. But instead of being spur-reduced there was a worm-drive at the top, with the steering wheel at the end of the short horizontal-shaft, spoked, like a ship's—which no doubt took a bit of turning! This tail-end monster had a modest success and there were exports. Experience soon showed, however, that only half the weight was necessary, and that 15-tons fitted most requirements. When it could be seen that even lighter ones still would do, Thomas Aveling took the obvious course of reverting to the traction engine; but not quite as it had become in its agricultural guise although this latter now had chain-and-roller steering single-speed threeshaft gearing, and was rather rangy looking.

The new traction-engine-type roller first seen in 1871 was more compact, with a smaller flywheel and had an extra shaft held in the extended firebox plates parallel with the crankshaft, and was, in fact, the first non-ploughing engine fourshaft. (Soon after that Claytons brought out their primitive fourshaft agricultural engine, previously mentioned, which was soon superseded by a threeshaft; Avelings meanwhile continuing with their threeshaft agricultural engines for several more years.) The chain-and-roller steering here had extention reels outside the holding brackets, around each of which the steering chains were coiled, a practice which was continued for many years before the familiar traction engine's crossed chains going round the roller inside the brackets was used. The smokebox plates were extended top and bottom, like an open mouth, to hold the 'stalk' for the front roller and this went right through to the axle. The two halves of the front roller were coned to allow for this space and to bring them together at the bottom: a not very good idea, but one which was prolonged after the familiar front 'stump' or saddle replaced the 'mouth'.

This allowed the stalk a certain amount of swing at the top, pendulum-wise, from a fulcrum at the bottom of the stump, and so avoiding the twisting action which occurred previously when the front roller encountered uneven ground.

Cylindrical front rolls, afterwards universal, only replaced the conical ones gradually, although they had been used on the Large-Framed-Roller. Here, one imagines thought first directed to the same cylindrical device to contain them and then it having to be discarded because of the extra length required. A fork to hold them nowadays looks obvious, particularly in its crossways form, used for half a century before the fore-and-aft semicircular one replaced it, and now seen on diesel rollers. But this had to be 'thought up' in the first place and as designers had less examples to draw on then with rule-of-thumb approaches to differing requirements. With a much shortened stalk for the fork there was a lessened risk of its snapping off; yet it did happen occasionally, right throughout its history. Going fast against an obstruction could do it, as also could towing from front axle height, particularly when jerked. (The proper way to tow a roller was by a push-pole chained round the stump and a man steering; or backwards, from the towing jaw behind the bunker.)

As a roller's best work is done when moving very slowly the gear ratio was made to suit this work, and it is possible that had low-loading lorries been available then a single gear would have sufficed.

But, of course, they had to move from site to site, and leave their site for picking up water or night parking. Thus was a second speed a more urgent requirement than on an agricultural engine, which spent a great percentage of its time on belt work. Aveling's design to suit his new fourshaft, was one which was adhered to for twenty years, and the forerunner of the standard two-speed gear change for fourshaft single cylinder engines. The crankshaft had its pinions spaced in the familiar places—low against the flywheel bearing, a space for neutral, and high close to the eccentrics. The second shaft was a fixed axle, over which was a collar holding the high and low pinions there, and the pinion which engaged the third shaft which was over to the right on an extension to the collar. This pinion was made wide, to be always in-mesh with its opposite, whichever way, right or left—for high or low gear—the collar was in. Its 'opposite' was inside the footplate, to enable this to be done, well shrouded and necessarily of small diameter for lack of room. The improved two-speed gear which eventually replaced it on Avelings and all others too, had a revolving second shaft with the sliding-pinions either keyed on to it or the shaft made square just there, as has been mentioned. This allowed the drive to the third shaft to be outside where there was room for the 'opposite' to be larger; thus could the primary crankshaft pinions be larger too and still preserve the same gear ratio, and as they were larger they did not wear so quickly. Another wearing point on fixed-shaft engines was first in the collar—lubricating this by oil-can through holes in it tending to be hit-and-miss, as the holes had to be worked round to be on top first. Then, when the collar became sloppy, it would cut into the shaft at the low-gear end. Also the wide pinion would wear, unevenly—as low gear was used the most—and with the mid-part never used, this being the neutral position; the teeth would stand out like a tuft of new grass in a lawn.

Few drivers found fault with this type of gear-change. Certainly no other moved in and out so easily and with the minimum of flywheel movement to get a 'fit', and it was seen on engines after the change-over from parallel slipper bars for the crosshead to cylindrical guides and after the regulator rod began to poke out of the far end of the cylinder, to the relief of many a driver going down a hill.

Scarifiers came in in the nineties, tank mounted on the off-side with a holding bar from an extension to the axle. When differentials were offered as an 'extra' ten years later, they had to be 'locked' by the differential pin previously described, when scarifying, to avoid wheelspin.

When it became evident that the agricultural engine, with wider uses in view would also have to have two speeds, Avelings, already with a two-speed fourshaft, discarded their threeshaft, instead of putting a second speed on it, as others had done, and followed the roller pattern with their traction engines. But with the larger flywheel required for this, the previous compactness of the roller was a slight drawback, as this had to go deeper down behind the rear wheel, a disadvantage for 'putting the belt on' and no improvement to looks.

Avelings were early with the double-engine system of steam ploughing, at first having the right-hand engine with flywheel and vertical-shaft on the right, which even at that time looked unorthodox. This way, however, there was no pull on the studs which held the bottom bracket of the vertical-shaft to the firebox plates, and a 'pushing action' instead, like on a left-hand engine's. Fowlers—except with a few 'specials'—always powered the rope-drum from the left, without any firebox trouble because of it, so Avelings were not long in following. Both-engines-the-same were cheaper to make, and also some owners changed them over periodically to equalise wear—where there would have been both with a pulling action on the studs if the older type were changed over! The first compounds, having valves-on-top like Fowler's, were 8nhps, rather small for the job, and retained the monkey-tail pull-up regulator of the singles—very sensitive, but a head-bumper when attending to the fire! The earliest of these had wooden front axles; pumps were driven direct from the crankshaft and crank balancing was an 'extra'. In 1905 the newer compounds with valves-on-the-sides began to appear on all Aveling tractions, rollers, and ploughing engines were then in larger sizes, which included the popular '16 nhps' for the home market. These had a push-and-pull upright regulator, a centre bearing between the close-together cranks, rather long reverse levers and a hand wheel for in-and-out of road gear instead of a lever, and were upstanding in the ploughing engine traditions. Aveling ploughing engines were rated second-best to Fowler & Co's in quality and a long way behind them in numbers, and like them, steered on the left.

Avelings were early too in the road engine field, both in singles and compounds and turned out some very large ones, and a few in showman's regalia. These were well liked by drivers and owners, but the firm did not persevere with them when the market began to fade in the early 1900s.

Their steam tractor was as good a five tonner as any made in this range, and planned so that it could be a convertible—tractor cum 8-ton roller—although it had rather a high top gear for a roller. In the latter role it was rather un-Aveling, in steering from the left. There was also an overtype steam wagon, well designed but seldom met with.

As Avelings were the first with steam rollers they were soon identified with them, and the large number of orders coming in from all parts of the world caused the firm to give this product priority. (Total roller production exceeded that of all the other makers together.) Thus often they were behind with satisfying orders for traction and ploughing engines, with the result that development and production here took rather a 'back seat'.

Even after the roller had crossed-chain steering, 2-speeds on the new pattern, trunk guides, compounds with valves-on-the-sides and 'straight grips' to the handles instead of 'shaped' handles, there were frequent modifications—as, indeed, one would expect with a machine made in such large numbers. Boilers got progressively smaller, an economy hardly noticed by the municipal driver. It was when long distances had to be travelled with van and water-cart between sites and often from one end of the country to another that this was most noticed, particularly with the compounds, which were not very good steamers and easy to prime.

Piston valves came in in the early twenties, and when in good order were fine and free running with but a modest demand on the boiler; and the singles had the added luxury of a balanced crank, giving improved appearance and smoother starting, which was important when one some materials, which could be marked by a jerky start. Properly handled there was no need for the more expensive compound then. These were made in 6, 8, 10, 12 and 14-ton sizes and properly trained drivers liked them best of all. In theory the piston valve is more efficient than the slide valve, and, as these in all known cases had inside admission, 'open rods', instead of 'crossed rods' from the eccentrics could be used with 'links down', as was the case with a threeshaft, which was another theoretical addition to efficiency, giving better steam distribution (and which will be mentioned in more detail later). In practice, however, where the majority of drivers lacked what amounted to a proper apprenticeship to the job, the piston valve was not such a success. They could suffer when dirty water was picked up from some roadside places, and unless the level was then kept to the minimum consistent with safety wet steam would get into the valve cylinder and bring grit with it to score the walls, where the spring loaded slide-valve here would come away from its face enough to prevent scoring. Thus did piston-valves and the surfaces they ran against suffer from frequent wear, when they would use more fuel than the slide-valve. The many complaints because of this caused Avelings to change back to slide-valves again in the early thirties: perhaps a retrograde step, but this roller was the sweetest running and easiest regulating and steering of all, and, sadly, so soon to be discontinued in favour of diesel engined machines, and clearly the best steam roller of any make of the 'traction engine type'.

Only with this last roller was thought given to pump design, where it was geared down and reliable, although still on the side of the boiler. Previously an Aveling pump was a finicky thing. Having no return pipe it was sucking air—and with a dry plunger—when the water was turned off. To get it going again air had often to be released from the top via a tap and driver's elongated extra control (besides his water tap). Many owners removed it, fitting an extra injector, and some rollers came new with two injectors instead of one and a pump. A variation of this on the older compounds was a straight-down pump on the firebox side from an eccentric behind the flywheel, which was a little more reliable.

Clayton & Shuttleworth

This firm was the earliest and largest of the Lincoln makers. As Thomas Aveling had used a Clayton portable for his first self-moving experiment there was a natural merging of developments. The first Clayton traction engines had their cylinders, both single and double, over the firebox, the steersman standing on the forecarriage. With the change from chain to gear drive the position was changed round with first a short period of chain and front steersman before the four-shaft previously mentioned. Then followed the early, or part-Fletcher threeshaft, which began to look like a traction engine rather than a converted portable and had the unusual feature of rack steering, which would be similar to operate to chain steering—more precise on the road—but hard to move on soft and uneven ground. This was produced 1891 to 1895 when it was replaced by the also mentioned Fletcher fourshaft, which many drivers thought was the best Clayton of all, although rather heavy on the rears. Unlike the Aveling side-mounted pump the one on this had a suction and return, and so did not give half the trouble. It was nice to look upon and had a handsome brass chimney top featuring the London & North Western

Railway engine shape of the period, cross-arm governors, a built-up crank instead of the usual forged one and a trunk guided smallend block replacing the four parallel bars.

A contemporary of this was a compound, first in road loco form, massive in appearance with 7ft rears 2ft wide. A Worthington steam pump on the boiler's offside supplemented the injector and a third speed and springs could be had as extras. A number were exported, but few used in this country. An agricultural version followed and overlapped a redesign of the single until it was replaced by one of more orthodox type. The valves were on top of the steam chest driven by radial gear of the Joy type, also a LNWR feature. Actuating rods from halfway along the connecting rods provided the motion and there was good steam distribution, and because there were no eccentrics, a saving in overall width. Here, in spite of the two cranks, a single's simpler inside gear-changing could be retained. Many drivers did not like these because of poor response to the reversing lever, which proved of little use for the quick stop with steam on, often so vital when manoeuvring for the belt to go on, with an audience of farm men waiting to start. "Give me Stephenson's link gear every time," they said, and, of course, it came at last, but rather late in the day.

About 1906 the Fletcher engine was revamped rather than re-designed into what became known as the post-Fletcher, although the great man was reputed to be with the firm after that time. The boiler and flywheel were smaller for the same nhp and the crank was forged. Pickering governors replaced the crossarms and there was an inside two-to-one geared-down pump—always a good feature, only the gears were strangely heavy for the job. The smokebox was an extension of the boiler shell, so that when the latter had its lagging on the former looked of smaller diameter (the earlier engine's smoke-box was flush with the lagging, a standard practice with most other makers except Fowlers). It also extended a little beyond the chimney; what with this, the larger front wheels and the relatively small flywheel which had curved spokes, there was something of the 'little ploughing engine' about this model.

It cut in less on soft ground and was more economical on the belt, but its 150lb working pressure was no compensation for the pre-decessor's larger boiler, even at 10lb less pressure, and the alterations proved to be overdone. The driver had to climb onto the road wheel to reach the flywheel for pulling it off a dead-centre, and unless the pressure was kept high—not always desirable for manoeuvring—

priming was a frequent occurrence. Of course, men got used to them, but coming to a Clayton from another make seldom led to early affection. Although 'slimmed', its overlarge fronts made it poor in the lock and several minor features, like the oversized pinions on the first and second shafts, and the greater than usual piston-rod diameter ($1\frac{3}{4}$in instead of $1\frac{7}{16}$) using precious cylinder space added up to 'over-massiveness' so that they were often deemed clumsy and awkward. There were modifications from time to time, one being the pump drive. Here the eccentric was on an extended sleeve to the low gear pinion, which was always in mesh with the one on the crank-shaft, and the other pair were similarly in mesh, so that in neutral—when threshing—these chinked round all the time. 'In-gear' meant the sliding of a dog, splined to the shaft, along into one or the other of the second shaft's pair and so locking it to the shaft to move it. Although this may have been a saving in manufacture it was referred to by many as 'A rare contrivance.'

About 1909 the new compound came out with valves on the sides of the steam chest. It was unusual in having square connecting rods and one of the link motions in between the cranks instead of both outside. This drove the valve for the left-handed high-pressure cylinder by a rocker arm which passed through the trunk guide just above the piston rod. The two minor advantages this gave were possibly not covered by the extra cost of manufacture, as the more straightforward way of other makers seemed adequate enough, with no observable loss of efficiency. The more obvious advantage was that it brought the hp crank close up to its bearing, and the other that the link-drive rods were 'open' instead of 'crossed' as was the case with fourshafts which ran in a forward direction with their links down. The rocker arm reversed the sequence (as do inside admission piston valves). The drive to the lp's link was by crossed rods in the normal way—otherwise one set would have been up when the other down! Had this not been so Claytons would doubtless have devised a double weigh-shaft on the see-saw plan, only then, one link would have been ahead of the other. "Worth it" they might have said "to balance out the movement"!

A large three-speed road loco was developed from this model, but only three made. There was also a steam tractor of the normal three-shaft pattern, which the firm had the courage to enlarge in the early twenties to take advantage of the increase in weight allowed. But it was then too late on the scene to aid sales.

Clayton did well with overtype wagons until the end of World

War I. They were unusual in having a piston valve for the hp cylinder and a slide valve for the lp and did not have the rocker-arm, but both link-drives outside. In the mid-twenties they passed wagons over to another company, Clayton Waggons Ltd where improvements were tried out and an undertype developed, with, however, little success.

Their steam rollers were not numerous and until the war was over were but modified traction engines. Soon after came a neat design as up-to-date as any which was just beginning to sell well in the later twenties when the firm went into liquidation. (Their cash-flow had never recovered from war exertions and the loss of payment for exports to Russia.) The firm of Babcock & Wilcox took over the last batch of these, which were beginning to sell well and added to it for a short time by others carrying their own nameplate. The threshing machine department went to Marshalls, where its chief value was in ceasing to be of competition, the Clayton thresher being rather the more popular of the two. Not until Marshalls produced their steel framed model a little before threshing was swamped out by combining, were any Clayton features brought in. Here they used the Clayton type awner, which was a decided improvement. There was nothing about any Clayton engine Marshalls would have wanted to have copied.

Charles Burrell & Sons

This firm depended on traction engines for its living, so had to be good. It can be said that everybody liked a Burrell, so much so that there were fans, just as Great Western Railway engines had theirs. Thus must investigation be cautious.

After a portable engine beginning there were self-movers which could have been developed into fast vehicles for haulage and passengers a decade before the steam wagon, had the law of the day allowed it. Boilers were also supplied for John Fowler's early experiments with ploughing by steam. Possibly because of this connection there were early Burrell single cylindered ploughing engines both chain and gear driven with four shafts and back-hand steering rather after the Fowler pattern, and also with chain-and-roller steering. These, of 8nhp, and 14nhp, did not reproduce themselves for long, although in later years ordinary traction engines fitted with side-drums for cable ploughing made a gesture rather than a 'comeback'.

Early as well with the ordinary traction engine, Burrells never departed from threeshafts here unless to special order in road-roller form. Unlike William Fletcher they deemed the extra width but a small disadvantage and that consideration should be given to the saving in power, with one shaft less to drive; there was sometimes a hint of another advantage too, as a threeshaft could have 'open rods' with its links down for forward running, which gave, theoretically, better steam distribution. The single cylinder agricultural engine in its 'modern form' had a wide gap between cylinder end and chimney to make the threeshaft's commonly longer connecting rod as short as possible and so preserve a better balance. It first came out new with a half-round iron ring at its chimney top, and later with a rather ugly rough-cast chimney, bell-topped, and very heavy (but one which did not burn-out). Governors were first cross-arm; then of the Burrell enclosed type, before eventually Pickerings were used and by Pickering days the chimney had improved to a shapely, rather 'full', copper topped one. Particularly handsome was the square-blocked crosshead, sliding between broad top and bottom bars, and the balanced big-end of the last-of-all ones; less so was the over-long reversing lever, pulled back, of course, in greater prominence, for the threshing position.

Not long before the turn of the century it was rumoured that a member of the family had a vision in church one Sunday morning, unfortunately not a very Christian revelation, although it conferred a benefit on mankind. This was perhaps inspired by the tandem compound stationary engine, 'doubled back', as it were, to save room. Both cylinders were cast in the same block, the smaller high pressure one above, with their rods leading to a common crosshead and valves to one set of link motions, so that the crankshaft-end was like a single's. Here was something cheaper than a double-crank compound, with many of its advantages, and ideal for threshing, giving more power for the same weight as a single, greater economy, a quieter exhaust and easiness to clean. This 'single-crank compound' became popular with all classes of user, and long ran parallel with the single in development, but was eventually ousted in favour by the double-crank compound. It had two faults; jerkiness of motion— alleviated when a balance-weight was fitted—and a poorly designed crosshead. This ran between the older fashioned double set of parallel bars to make it flat enough for the piston rods to join it above and below, and after some wear the massive gudgeon-pin would be partly riding on the bars. Some owners would shim this up with brass, widening the bar distance a little. When run at low pressure the thrusts of the two pistons were unequal, which was transmitted to the crosshead, and on some engines gave rise to what became known as the 'Burrell thump', which was difficult to eradicate by adjustment. It is a pity they did not give this crosshead 'another think'.

(Long after Burrells ceased, compounds of this type were being made by the German firm of Ruthemeyer of Soest, near Hamm, for threeshaft rollers. They claim never to have heard of Burrell, to have negotiated with Fowler for the idea, and to have improved the crosshead, which ran between top and bottom bars of normal spacing, which kept the gudgeon pin off the latter, and the 'thump' from happening.)

The 5nhp 'Devonshire' was the best known single crank compound threshing engine, popular in the West Country where the lanes were narrow and load behind the thresher light—usually no more than a straw tyer. But for heavier conditions the 6nhp of this type was the best Burrell agricultural engine; the 7nhp was more than adequate, and 8s and 10s rather heavy for anything but haulage.

Burrell agricultural traction engines were everywhere in Norfolk, and with a fair scattering in the rest of the country; yet the firm's speciality was road locomotives. As these began to drift slowly out of favour for general haulage in the late '90s a new market for them in showman's form was developing, in which the firm gained a monopoly. They had, of course, rivals in this field, Fowlers being the biggest, but who made less than half as many showmen. But fair-ground buyers took less kindly to the single crank compound, holding that the double crank was smoother when driving the dynamo; Burrells were early with a very good one of these too with, as has been mentioned, valves on the sides.

The road loco had all the trimmings—springs back and front, belly tanks and three speeds. The latter's triple pinions on the outside of the crankshaft looked rather weighty, but the bearing was wide for this so no harm resulted. The back-axle had patent coil springs underneath it. Its spurs were held in-mesh with the countershafts by a connecting bar on the near side (where the final drive was: some engines had a double final drive) which moved with the springs' action—until it came undone: fortunately a rare occurrence. A loose set-screw has been known to allow the top holding pin to jostle-out on the road. Then a tyro would soon understand what pulling-into-gear meant and the catastrophic opposite, as 'she'd ride her gears' on reverse loading, like holding with the lever down-hill

or trying to go backwards! (A threshing engine once did this on a
hill and miraculously kept on the road with all the tackle behind it
'at bike's free-wheel speed'; it pulled itself in gear on the next up-
gradient; negotiated a field gateway in one swing; pulled the drum
between two ricks; failed to line-up and get the belt distance the
first time, but did it on the second, all without once being able to go
backwards. A repair was soon made in such a way that it did not
happen again; but that man's eyes were always snapping up and
down and everywhere, when on the road, thenceforth.)

Coil sprung threshing engines would sometimes 'lift a shoulder'
with every rev when on the belt. A way of dealing with this was to
put a block under a wheel and jack up tight against it from the
opposite side of the other wheel. This could put the flywheel out of
alignment with the drum unless allowance was made in the last foot
of lining-up for the belt by turning in or out as needs be. Coil springs
also dug in on mud and made the wheels kick and judder when fully
spudded. Threshing drivers did not like them very much.

The Burrell steam tractor, which came out before the weight limit
was extended to five tons, was, like the Aveling, 'as good as any in
its class'. When the weight limit was raised they made a larger
tractor, almost in the 5nhp range, but the market for these had gone
for anything to come of it. The wagon, orthodox looking, as with
Aveling's, was not often seen.

The roller, a little wide because of being a threeshaft, had to have
a wider front roll, which made for harder steering. Made in single,
sc compound and dc compound forms it was, of course a good one, as
was everything made by Burrells; but there were not very many of
them. A relatively small firm which specialised, as did Burrells with
their showman, were often confined to this at the expense of market-
ing other types. Most of the makers specialised, when, unless they
were a large firm, their other models seemed to suffer.

Burrell engines steered from the left, some having footplate
entrance from this side and other from the right, when the steersman
had his own steps; the pump was also on the left (other than the
geared-down one). The firehole had doors which slid open by a hand
lever, and which, after periods of banking-up (the fire left in all night,
with the chimney lid, or 'top' on) would get tar along its bottom
slide, which had to be poked out on occasions before the doors would
move.

William Foden

This firm, afterwards to become Fodens Ltd, began its steam career
with portables. It also hired out threshing tackle, driven by sons of
the founder. The first-hand experience gained was later invaluable
when the Foden traction engine came into being, late in the day for
tractions and so, modern in appearance. This was a fourshaft and the
compound had outside valves and a 'double high' arrangement as
described under 'Steam Wagons', but, of course, an innovation then.
Various aspects in the Stevenson's reversing-gear followed well tried
railway practice and gave greater efficiency than other TEs of the
day enjoyed, although the gear was similar in appearance.

The flywheel was well down behind its large rear wheel, like an
Aveling's and there was the distinctive feature of springs mounted
above, at driver's eye level, which at first proved of great danger
whenever a shackle from these came undone; but this allowed good
ground clearance. Foden tractions were well liked by hauliers and
threshing contractors, but soon discontinued, as this was a competitive market and their newly begun overtype steam wagon was
crying out for all the resources which could be devoted to it—another
example of a speciality stealing the show.

No-one ever gave the Foden wagon a 'bad word', and the impression is given that other makers only came in because Fodens had
surprised them by discovering such a big market. There is no question
that in all its stages it was the best one of its type, and always ahead
of others. Its better steaming, economy and liveliness is not a little
due to the carefully designed valve-gear of the TEs. The boiler was
unsurpassable. It could on occasions gobble the coal but always
supplied the steam. Foden wagons were manufactured with the
latest machine tools available and spares could be had off-the-shelf
and easily fitted by customers' staff.

Later wagons had their pressure increased to 250lb, three-speeds
and Ackerman steering on left- or right-hand sides, whichever preferred, when the flywheel and gearing followed suit. There was a
tractor version of this, the 'D' which had larger wheels; lower gear
ratios; and a rather cumbersome back-axle wire rope and linked-
together sets of spuds. Its life was a short and happy one in the
timber trade until diesels came along, when some were fitted with
governors and went threshing. This they did with gusto, the high
pressure giving ample power even for threshing-and-cutting as
well as for getting along the roads at high speed (necessitating rubber

tyres on thresher and elevator) and the large tank lasting ten hours or so on the belt, which saved much water carrying; but diesel power soon took over here too, as this was the thirties. The Foden tractor cannot be compared with orthodox tractors which were really scaled-down road locos and practically extinct before it was born. It had nearly twice the power and speed and although Robey & Co. turned out a few similar ones there was no tractor really to compare with the Foden 'D'.

William Foster

This firm were the last in Lincoln—or, indeed, anywhere—to be making tractions, which they did until the late thirties, with little alteration in basic design and characteristics. Their first were three-shafts with left-hand steering, slipper bar guided crossheads and fron wheels set back under the boiler. The valve-rods were round instead of in bar form; regulator straight across and Push to start; governors crossarm; and safety valves large, with the top connecting-bar extending equally on either side. Late in this period there were a few engines with Starkey's valve-gear, which differed from the Stephenson's by having one eccentric. The straight-up regulator was linked to a chimney-end entrance to the steam chest. A cord from here would often go as far as the top of the threshing machine, so that the feeder could pull it to stop the tackle in an emergency: a peculiar Lincolnshire safety device this, as whatever damage was being done, the drum's momentum would be prolonging it for a long minute before the machinery came to rest. There really was no substitute for a driver's alertness.

By the early 1900s there was a change to fourshafts on the 6, 7 and 8nhp sizes, and ten years later to trunk-guided crossheads. After World War I—when the firm had made the first tanks, because of previous experiments with a tracked traction engine—the front axle was moved forward. This improved the appearance and lessened lifting and slewing in front but put more weight on the rears. (At this time the emblem of the military tank as a reminder of war service was added to the smokebox door lettering.) Thus the Foster became not too good on soft ground and, because of its large boiler, was often dubbed 'long and awkward' by those who did not know it well, with sometimes the additional epithets of 'sluggish' and 'coal burner' because of a somewhat tardy governor response, and the large grate area. To the casual glance there was little difference in size between these three, other than the rear wheels which were

5ft 10in by 16in wide; 6ft by 16in wide; and 6ft 2 inby 18in wide
respectively. All had a 12in stroke, but progressively larger bores, and
the 8nhp a larger diametered boiler. The 5nhp known as 'The
Little Gem' remained a threeshaft, possibly because extra width—if
this was a consideration—was of no inconvenience on this small
engine, with a 10in stroke and 14in wide wheels.

The 7nhp single cylinder agricultural engine was as large as some
makers' 8s, and as strong, and from the driver's angle there was
never a better one. Gentle on the regulator; obedient to the reverse
lever; 'live' on the crank, which would start on a desired direction in
almost any position; a splendid steamer; plenty of boiler room—
making for long intervals between firing and feed-water adjustments—and a non-primer, unless all the rules were broken, like
backing up-hill with a full glass, and low in steam. As much as half a
barrow of coal could be shovelled into its bars before starting out on
the road and the pressure gauge needle then kept in place by an
ease up or down of the ashpan lid, handle providing this could be
pegged into position by a nail. (A frequent driver's modification was
to drill small holes for this near the handle-end guide, as there were
no notches there. Full open or full shut did not seem an adequate
choice of positions, but was the one adhered to by the makers.) A
reliable three-valve pump (most pumps had two) on the right, close
to the floor was sloped for a straight connection to its eccentric and
the throw of this in-line with the crank, so that looking down on the
motion it all seemed to be 'coming over together'. A 90° difference
here would have given the illusion of better balance; actually, in spite
of long connections and no weights opposite the big-end, the motion
was well balanced, the heavy and rather wide flywheel and being an
influence. Supplementing the pump was a $\frac{3}{4}$in injector at the tank
base.

In general, when a piston rod did not extend through the far
cover there was a slight difference between the exhaust beats, one
being a little the heavier and this the first, thus, 'Chuff-chuff, Chuff-
chuff, Chuff-chuff.' With most Fosters, however, it was the other
way round, 'chuff-Chuff, chuff-Chuff, chuff-Chuff', which gave a
cheerful syncopation when on the belt and a sort of hop-and-skip
recovery rather than a slog when a semi-opened sheaf had gone
down the drum, and looking at the 'togetherness', or even knowing
it was there, when threshing, added emphasis to the rhythm.

It was an easy engine to keep clean, and chaff and thistle-down
collecting in the crank-pit could be raked out with the mud-hoe

(used when washing-out the boiler) through a hole conveniently placed on either side of the back-plate. Most crops could be threshed on no more than 100lb of steam, and blowing-off was a rare occurrence as the pressure never gained once the ashpan lid was shut, and its maximum of 140lb rarely needed. The rods and brasses were always rather dull, no matter how much work went into them; the chimney was too large and sometimes surmounted by an oversized copper top; the smokebox had no protecting baffle plate inside, and perhaps because of burning here the last few engines had this extending in front of the chimney; these also had aluminium covers on cylinder head and valve plate, with regulator again straight across 'with a crink in it' after a twenty-year mid-period of being turned upward at the handle end. The firehole door opened and shut by hinge and latch, with no chain on, as it was doubtless assumed that drivers' fingers would be calloused! There was no blower pipe going into the chimney base to hasten steam raising—or tubes leaking— and whenever the regulator was opened steam would sing pleasantly into the cylinder, and, if not under load when it was shut, the rings would go 'Clipple-clopple-clipple-clopple', clean, metallic and relaxed until the motion came to rest. The rather low-geared steering wheel had a brass handle and the oil-pump a hinged lid which opened all-of-it, so that the thick cylinder oil could be readily poured-in instead of going drop by drop through a narrow aperture. On the whole it was a plain, simple, yet well thought-out engine, soft in its exhaust with a most musical note to its gearing and one with which a man could form a faithful happy, and lifelong relationship.

Foster compounds, always with valves-on-top (except on their steam wagons), were occasionally in 5 and 6nhp sizes for agricultural use and always on the larger road locos. Pickering governors were here fitted as standard and, of course, springs and belly-tanks too. These were mostly in showman's form and well liked, especially the large 10nhp Scenic with generators fore and aft of the chimney. They were never so popular here as Burrells and Fowlers, as it was thought—however erroneously—that they wore-out quicker.

Their Wellington tractor was as 'good as any other maker's'—the 5-ton limitation restricting much difference in design. They sold well until the law permitted an increase to 7-tons, when, as there was no modification, they were less competitive.

The overtype steam wagon was never popular, being late with in what were, in the twenties, modern trends, although they did just achieve Ackerman steering and a third speed before being dropped from production.

Fosters never produced a steam roller, yet tractors owner-converted to rollers have been seen. The best known of these was a special double cylindered one after it had been used for Richard Hornsby's experiments as a track-layer. (*see R. Hornsby.*)

Fowell & Co

This business was started late in Queen Victoria's reign by a member of Burrell's staff and made 6, 7, and 8nhp single tractions. They were lh steered threeshafts and had many Burrell features, except the crosshead, which was trunk-guided, and the front axle, which remained throughout well set-back under the boiler. Thus although they were not good looking they were light underfoot and short in the lock, an advantage which balanced-out 'rearing' in an area where most corn ricks were on soft ground. Too much moving about then to get into position would mean ruts which could often imprison the steering. In such conditions a rear-heavy engine with a wide turning circle would show up at its worst, even if it was more sure-footed on the road.

An optional extra was a third, lower, gear. With the ordinary gears in neutral, a gearing-down double pinion would mesh with the crankshaft's small one, an insertion which made the engine a temporary fourshaft, with the reverse lever then in the back position to go forward. So slow could then be the resulting movement that the driver could get off and hold a lump of wood under a sinking-in wheel until a spud gently tightened up on it to lift the engine out and so avoid the kicking movement a higher gear gave which so often disrupted wheel packing.

A variation was a road engine which used the Box Patent System, where the cylinder was over the firebox, like a portable's. Gearing from the crankshaft came down to a jack-shaft half way along the chassis with disks on either side. Locomotive type coupling rods were on these and along to the rear wheels on a sprung axle, which did not then upset the gearing in its movement, as the jack-shaft could remain rigid no matter how the other's 'up-and-downing' went: a tortuous patent, indeed!

Fowells only made one or two engines a year, their main business being the erection and repair of Fenland pumping engines, and few who were not Fenland dwellers knew them, although these always spoke well of them. Where most wheel slats pointed upward when viewed from the rear; Fowells always had theirs slanting the opposite way.

John Fowler & Co

Once this company 'got off the ground' with its double engine system of steam ploughing—which proved the only satisfactory way—it grew rapidly. Kitsons, the neighbouring railway locomotive builders, replaced Claytons and Burrells as boiler makers and eventually made most of the engine, and were then later themselves replaced by Fowlers doing all their own manufacturing in the famous 'Steam Plough Works'.

A few portables were made, looking like embryo tractions, with the cylinder at the chimney end, as well as metre and full gauge rail locos, but most of their efforts were with traction engines, and of these the already mentioned ploughing engines predominated, in great variety.

Although Fowlers tried to avoid the loose nhp rating by using a code of letters for their ploughing engines, drivers were not to be taken in! There were four basic sizes of singles, '8s, 12s, 14s, and 16s'. The 8s had a straight spoked flywheel, a right-hand cylinder, pull-up 'monkey tail' type regulator and worm and chain steering. The others had curved spoked flywheels and, generally, back-hand steering. Variations were rh or lh cylinder, the latter looking better, as it was nearer the point where the hard work was done. This type generally had a straight-up push and pull regulator handle linked, and further levered, to a steam chest entrance at the chimney end; but sometimes a monkey-tail one and with the link-motion Up for going forward (with lever also then forward) to which later reference will be made. Right-hand cylindered engines had the mt regulator. Other differences were 'top change' and tapered dog clutch on the vertical-shaft (previously mentioned), and 'right way' and 'wrong way' sloping wheel strakes.

Compound PEs for the home market had codes which would have fitted nhps in even numbers up to 20nhps, with the AAs and BBs being the favourites. The former had its low-pressure piston rod extending through the cylinder head and the typical Fowler broad top-and-bottom bars for the crossheads to slide in. The BB had a single slide-bar suspending the crosshead beneath it, and the later, rather heavier BB1, also with its lp piston-rod going through the far end. Variations were 'super-heaters', where the chimney was at

the end of the smokebox instead of being set-back; two speeds on
the rope drum (the smaller vertical-shaft bevel coming up from
inside the other to engage an adjoining crankshaft bevel); and
piston valves, operated by single eccentric reversing gear and often
those with old-fashioned-looking safety valves (these too had super-
heaters and were not much liked). What few drivers knew was that
cylinder diameters could vary, some being bored smaller than
standard to suit special conditions, so that what was thought a '16'
could well be a '14'. Then there were variations of ratio to the rope
drive. One would think the large diameter choice of cylinder better
suited for the slower running motion of a high geared model, but
there is no sign of the firm having explored this line of thought, which
a computer might have done. There is no doubt that where the
ground was stiff and pulls long, the smaller diametered cylinder was
to be preferred, even if it meant wing-tines off the 'drag'. The engine
then seldom ran out of steam on a long pull.

Compound PEs had clutch-on-the-vertical-shaft rope drum engagement, with some large export models clutch-on-the-crankshaft,
which was similarly handled to the single's top-change, and all had
chain-and-roller steering.* Later ones had the gentlest of regulators,
straight-up or slanting, pull to start, the steam chest at the driver's
end. This ironed-out the risk of the jerkiness sometimes caused by an
unskilled hand: pleasing, this, for the man on the implement after a
turn at the far end, when the lever for dropping it could be reached-
for without fear of overbalancing!

The BB was a handsome and well proportioned engine, and, like
so many things looking just right, really was Just Right.

The agricultural engines merited less praise. The earliest were
threeshafts with lh steering, large portable engine type governors
and 'wrong way' wheel strakes, sometimes varied with two rows of
alternating square blocks instead, and a very few with lh cylinder
and rh flywheel. A fourshaft with rh steering followed, which was the
maker's pattern for tractions thenceforth, although tractors and the
rollers which sprang from them had lh steering. A compound
appeared in the mid-nineties with the valves-on-top plant which
Fowlers originated, and a new single, variously designated a '7' or
an '8'. This generally had a 5ft flywheel, where 4ft 6in was cus-
mary; compound-type big-end—narrower than normal for a single;
and often small boiler—to save weight, cost, or both. It handled
nicely in level and hard rickyards, and was very economical, due

---

* i.e. same as 'warm and chain'.

more to the newly designed sensitive governor than the slower speed of its flywheel. On hard going, however, it was always short of steam, and would readily prime, even with head up-hill, and the narrow big-end had to have constant attention. The regulator was pull to start, straight across, and the hand-brake on the second shaft effective. The steersman had to learn not to move his wheel by the rim but by the handle on it, or else he would soon foul his hand on the close-up horizontally mounted pump. This model began what came to be familiar Fowler silhouette—'upstanding' large front wheels; a small diameter smokebox i.e. flush with the boiler shell, lagging making the boiler look thicker (seemingly copied by Claytons); a large chimney, often surmounted by the handsome 'rolled over' brass top; and a straight-down back to the bunker—limiting the coal space: the maker's signature written all over it, as it were. This was not a well-liked engine. A larger boilered one came out in 1904, and a wider and 6in less diameter flywheel became standard five or six years later, when there was then a choice of regulator to the compound's 7 o'clock (and sometimes 5 o'clock) hanging-down type. Then it could be called a good engine, if a bit rear heavy and ungainly.

Despite these drawbacks Fowler agricultural engines were seen in all districts, especially where large farmers had their own threshing sets, or steam plough owners did some threshing too, and liked to stay with the same make (most steam ploughs being Fowlers). The spares service was excellent, and exploded drawings available, where parts could be picked out by number and code and ordered by telegram. Thus less skilled maintenance was required than with some other makes. Threshing machine owners, on the whole, did not prefer them, having more time in the off-seasons to make-do-and-mend on engines which they regarded as 'handier'.

Fowler Road Locomotives under the name 'Lion' were specially designed as such and first seen as two-speed 7 and 8nhp compounds in the Boer War period, adopted to military specifications. This saved them from the fate of other mammoths, as about then road locos for general purposes, for a variety of reasons, not least of which was the steam wagon, were becoming extinct. These developed into the famous B6, with a third speed outside the near horn plate, and a flywheel gracefully dished to receive it.

Both types tried hard in showman's regalia. They did not catch up with Burrell here, coming second, with half as many. But the firm had the larger overall production of road locos being almost alone in the specialist heavy haulage field until the low-loading lorry came, in the thirties. A pair of Lions would sometimes be seen coupled together in front of a large piece of power-station equipment, with another following drawing a living-van and supplies truck, and acting as an extra on steep hills.

Some took their pump drive from an eccentric on the second shaft, thus saving it from harm when revving in low gear. In showman's form the pump was separately geared-down so that it would work when out of gear, on the belt, instead of having then to rely solely on the injector.

The change to lh steering on the last four showmen emphasised that side, which kept the kerb in view, was preferable for a two-man engine, and overcame a long Fowler tradition of rh steering.

A smaller brother, the Tiger Tractor was designed after World War I when the weight limit was raised to 7-tons, but it did not appear soon enough to sell well, except in steam roller form. This had a single guide crosshead bar like the BBs.

There was a wide range of rollers besides these, singles and compounds closely following traction engine patterns until the twenties, when neater and more compact models were to be seen with trunk guides replacing the Fowler bars and generally in compound form some with one lever gear-change and others with two. Fowler rollers may have tied with Marshalls' in being second in production to Avelings.

An attempt was made at an undertype steam wagon having a front vertical boiler like a Sentinel's and an unusual V-twin engine behind the driver, shaft-driving the back-axle and mostly as Gully Emptiers, they sold 'in penny numbers', but did not 'get going' as haulage units.

Richard Garrett

This very old established family firm was the first to make a 'production model' threshing machine; thus they were as early as any with portable engines and only a short distance behind with tractions. Because of the wide range of their engineering products, however, the latter were never numerous.

The fourshaft agricultural model had Pickering governors from the turn of the century; the crosshead was trunk guided and there was usually left-hand steering. Their rear wheel halves were 'double laced', thin slats underneath being riveted through to those on top, which could give the illusion that the latter were 'crimped', or corrugated; a sound enough arrangement, perhaps, but weight adding.

There were some roller versions in the 6nhp range, and outside valve compound haulage engines which suffered teething troubles—mostly from insufficient bearing space in the motion—at a time when haulage engines, even in showman's form, were difficult to sell. The thick rimmed flywheel was 'more forrard and deeper in' (the rear wheel) than most and the copper chimney top shallow in depth; the same shape above as below; and sharp featured! It was a compact and handy engine, yet never popular.

What was popular was the Garrett Compound Steam Tractor, which came out the soonest after the weight limit had been increased to 7 tons, little single cylindered tractors being then long out of production. Haulage firms using tractors went for these as replacements, and they also touched the threshing market (not previously tractor work) where farmers liked their lightness of foot and economy even if drivers found them a little too light on the road and needing a close eye all the time when on the belt. In spite of seeming rather slow, with only two speeds, this was no great disadvantage in a modestly powered machine, which could rarely take a heavy load behind in a 'third wheel' if there were any hills. A curious feature were arrows on the steering wheel indicating that this should be turned clockwise for a right turn and anti-clockwise for a left!

Garrett overtype steam wagons were unusual with piston valves and always having steering and flywheel on the right. As piston valves required steam as dry as possible there was generally a superheater too, in the flat topped smokebox. This was a good wagon but early abandoned for the undertype, where a great effort was made to rival the Sentinal. They never succeeded in doing this, however. (Sentinel Wagons, Shrewsbury, with but few exceptions, made undertypes and are outside the scope of this survey.)

Richard Hornsby

This firm made many portables but few tractions, beginning late and leaving while still in the threeshaft era—their's being unusual for a threeshaft in having right-hand steering. The fronts were set back under the boiler, ugly, but seldom off-putting for a driver frequently 'in the soft'. They were among the first to drop steam entirely for oil engines and later conceived the now familiar crawler-track, with Fosters making 5nhp double high-pressure cylinder engine to fit in the frame. Hence Fosters tanks, and hence subsequent development by the American caterpillar firm! They pioneered a compression ignition model before Dr Diesel. At the end of World

War I they merged with Ruston, Proctor & Co of Lincoln, which
became 'Ruston-Hornsby'.

Few makers have a like interpretation of Nominal Horse Power,
but R. Hornsby differed between their own portables and tractions,
giving the former bigger cylinders for the same 'Horse Power' perhaps
to compensate for the larger flywheels and slower running. Boiler
pressures are not mentioned viz:

TRACTION ENGINES				PORTABLE ENGINES		
Flywheel		Cylinder		Flywheel	Cylinder	
		diameter	stroke		diameter	stroke
5hp	4ft	8	10	4ft 7in	$7\frac{3}{4}$	12
6hp	4ft 6in	8	12	5ft 1in	$8\frac{1}{2}$	12
8hp	4ft 6in	9	12	5ft 1in	10	12
10hp	4ft 6in	10	12	5ft 1in	11	14

J. & H. McLaren

A late comer into the industry this, producing their first single
cylinder ploughing engines in 1877, the former being remarkably
like a rh cylinder Fowler with monkey tail regulator, back-hand steering and top-change. The first threshing engine was a threeshaft with
slipper-bar crosshead and set-back wheels, remarkably heavy on the
rears, in spite of so much weight going onto the front. A variation
was sprung back-wheels, which did not help the weight problem
either.

The later fourshaft was handsomer, with wheels 'forard', a 'trunk
guide', and very like a Foster with rods instead of bars between
link motion and eccentrics; the safety valve lever extended equally
beyond both valves; the governors were identical and the handling
just as good. Differences were a less heavy-looking chimney, with a
kind of elongated Garrett top with less flare, sometimes of brass and
sometimes of plain metal; the regulator a straight across tuned-up
iron bar; the reverse-lever round, like a Marshall's; and wheel slats
with little rake to them. Rear-heaviness was a disadvantage and
agricultural engines had left-hand steering. Some of the compounds
had extra wide wheels to dilute this, which then added to the width
and was not a desirable feature either.

Their road loco was well liked but not numerous. Weight was of less disadvantage here; steering was generally on the right, with the reversing lever on that side too. Drivers with the habit of never letting go of the steering wheel in any circumstances, found this fault more difficult to sustain here. But those who liked to see the crank turning over first before taking a hand from a lever to grasp the wheel, soon became used to it!

The compound ploughing engine differed from Fowler's in having rh steering; outside valves; and a double vertical-shaft for two speeds. The gears did not slip into mesh so easily as the Fowler clutch and were harder to disengage. As this meant two bearings instead of one on the firebox side, this was subjected to strains which sometimes caused the stays to leak.

McLaren engines were particularly massive, which, if it helped sales abroad was a hindrance at home. Their catalogues showed engines hauling wagon trains across large tracks of Australia, and winding them through New Zealand highlands, with glowing letters from owners on how they never broke down, nor even wore out.

There were a few traction-type steam rollers, and tractors, the latter unusual both in being fourshafts and having rh steering and some with superheating.

In the cable ploughing field they stayed later than Fowler's, having earlier provided oil engine drive as an alternative to steam, and so extending their market. They also then supplied spares for all types of Fowler ploughing tackle when the latter 'changed their image' to crawler tractors. When this went out too the firm concentrated on large diesel engines for industrial and marine use.

Marshall, Sons & Co

Marshalls were a close rival to Claytons, making rather fewer threshing machines and more tractions, rollers, portables and stationary engines. At the turn of the century their catalogues said "75,000 engines and boilers supplied" and Claytons' "58,000 engines and machines sold."

Later starters with traction engines, they brought these sooner to fruition, and Marshall engines were generally preferred. The first model was an undertype—like a rail loco geared to traction wheels—which was soon followed by a period threeshaft, with set-back fronts, even then having a trunk guided crosshead, which only came later with most other makes. A fourshaft replaced this in the nineties which altered little until the last one in the early 1930s. It began with a spectacle plate in front of the crankshaft-holding horn plates; the crankshaft extended outside the rh bearing (incidentally, both permanent Allchin features); a straight across pull-to-start regulator; a hinged firehole door; and sparse footplate room. Around 1912 the regulator and gear change had an upright handle at the end of the straight-across piece; the firehole had sliding doors opening with a kick (Burrells had a longer handle there), but which, when the bottom slide blocked with coal dust, needed many kicks more, a patent cambered-top firebox, and curved spokes to the flywheel on the 5, 6, and 7nhp sizes; and more room in the footplate. In the late twenties the hinged firehole door, straight-across regulator and shortened footplate reappeared. Features remaining constant were a rounded reversing lever—as had McLarens—with 'Working Position' on a small brass plate under the middle notch of the three, forward and backward; a round-bar turned up at one end, instead of a brake-wheel, which was seldom used other than for hanging fireirons on; crossarm governors, more sensitive than most; a slightly slopping pump inside the footplate on the right (the usual fourshaft position) with a wheel instead of a handle to regulate it, generally driver-notched for a keep-even position when threshing; and, unless specially ordered otherwise, rh steering, with a larger than average wheel. An injector was not standard. There was a 'Q Type' appearing at intervals between 1912 and 1930 with Pickering or Gardner governors; a feed water heater; piston valve, and sometimes a set-back front axle.

The flywheels of the above sizes were 4ft 4in and of the 8nhp 4ft 9in and these latter had straight spokes to them, and a stayed-top firebox, the cambered-top being unsuitable for this larger size.

Road locos were not specially designed, but were tractions with added springs and belly tanks, and where three speeds were ordered, the flywheel was a solid one. (It was held that spoked flywheels frightened horse traffic, thus most makers had solid or blocked-in flywheels on their haulage engines and rollers, retaining spokes on threshing engines because it was then easier to get the belt on).

Compounds were made from the turn of the century, resembling Fowler's pattern, with inside links and valves-on-top, and distinguished by crossways safety valves and a steam chest secured to a machined flat surface by heavy bolts. Mostly ordered for rollers, this may have influenced a lower gear ratio, which was a source of driver-irritation on a compound threshing engine, unless there were three speeds.

The road wheels of the 6nhp singles were 6ft diameter and 16in wide. The 6nhp compound had them 2in wider, as did the 7nhp single, and the 8s a 6in increase in diameter.

The best Marshall engine for threshing was the 6nhp single (adequate, and lighter than the 6nhp compound). Carrying 150lb working pressure instead of the customary 140lb, it was stronger than the average 'six', although double work with a blower on the chaff cutter (when behind the thresher) made it bark out loud and clear through its non-tapered chimney with the gently flared deep-down brass top. On a normal day's work it was a hundred-weight of coal to the good when compared with, say, a Foster. Like a Foster, it would start in most crank positions, but obeyed its reverse lever less precisely, and was snatchy on the regulator, in spite of the long handle to give it sensitivity. Although it was not a 'big boilered engine' there was always enough steam, and it seldom primed or sunk in on soft ground, and only suggested a front-end lift on an uphill start. It was a handy engine in tight places, with the controls set close together to suit one-man driving.

Like most makers, Marshalls were early with a single-cylindered steam tractor, which they long kept on in roller form after this size had had its short life as a tractor. There was also a popular 5-ton tractor, which, too, became the basis of a light roller. Like most tractors, these were threeshafts steered from the left, and their performance improved with piston valves, generally coupled to Marshall's Patent Single Eccentric Radial Reversing Gear—claimed to give better steam distribution—with an unadvertised additional advantage of being cheaper to make.

Only in the last phase, when it was 'Rollers Only' and hardly a traction being made, and these singles, did Marshalls follow the trend and have valves-on-the-sides for compound fourshafts. Certainly then, the single eccentric was an advantage, giving room for wider big-end bearings and inside-pinion (a compound's 2nd gear pinion was generally outside, as with a threeshaft). The fourshaft rollers were handsome machines with a geared-down pump, and unlike Avelings, kept their piston valves to the last. The firm also flirted with a verticle boilered tandem and a 'Universal,' a horizontally boilered quick reverse 3-wheeled roller with enclosed motion.

A feature of the square—in profile—Marshall crosshead was a wedge-shaped adjustment both top and bottom which looked designed to take-up wear. As cylindrical guided crossheads on any make, kept properly lubricated, seldom got 'sloppy,' one can only suppose this was more for an aid to lining-up when erecting, although doubtless salesmen would indicate it as something to make the cross-head 'everlasting'.

Mann & Charlesworth

This small general engineering firm made a few tractions and portables but never really got into their stride until the steam wagon era, when the name was altered to Mann's Patent Steam Cart & Wagon Co.

There were original features: valves overhead (with cylinders outside); four shafts instead of three, with gear changes between the two countershafts instead of outside between crankshaft and counter-shaft; pump eccentric on the first countershaft which was in con-stant mesh with the crankshaft; rack-and-pinion steering instead of worm-and-chain (the rack curved round the turntable); no foot-plate, the driver sitting on the offside and mate the other, with his own steering wheel for use for when the driver fired up through his on-the-side door; a pipe from the safety-valve leading horizontally into the chimney; and single eccentric 'slip' reversing gear, with straight across lever. A later modification was the more usual steam chest with valves outside, using the better steam distributing Stephenson's reversing gear, with straight-up lever; and soon after, the second steering wheel and 'blowing off up the chimney' were discarded.

Because of the extra countershaft the engine went round in an opposite direction from other wagons; eliminating the footplate meant a shorter turn and that the fire could be cleaned out by stand-ing on the ground, instead of banging knuckles in a restricted space and often burning boots and trouser bottoms from spilled clinker; sitting on the side gave a better view ahead and behind; and the rack steering was more positive. In spite of these various innova-tions—the first, for what it was worth, gave open rods to the valve-gear—the wagon did not sell anything like Foden's or even catch-up Claytons or Allchins. Many customers were flour-millers, where the loads were relatively light.

There was a tractor, which apart from the safety-valve extension to the chimney and rack-and-pinion steering, looked like any other; and an agricultural steam tractor, or 'Steam Cart' which closely followed the wagon and its modifications, although there was no pro-vision for a mate and his second steering wheel. Hopefully made with

direct ploughing in mind, among other duties—steam never succeeded here—it was a useful little threshing engine. The lh flywheel
was larger than the wagon's and the driver got it in line by siting
the frame ahead of him with various features on the thresher's corn-
end. The axle was close up, gear driven and had a rope-drum
in the middle. Wide traction wheels were of small enough diameter
to go underneath the large water tank, surmounted by a coal bunker
high up behind the driver; the fronts were set close together, to avoid
fouling the belt when driving a low-down saw bench; and there
were Pickering governors. Fuel consumption was better than a
traction's and, considering its light weight, it got its tackle about
well. It was more popular on large farms which did their own
threshing than with the threshing contractor.

Ransomes, Sims & Jefferies

Founded by Robert Ransome, blacksmith and implement maker,
in the late eighteenth century, this firm, after a portable engine
beginning, were making threeshaft tractions a hundred years later,
as Ransome, Sims & Head, with set-back fronts, a slipper bar crosshead and curved spokes to flywheel and steering wheel. When
William Fletcher joined them he cleaned up this design in an exercise not dissimilar to his fourshaft Clayton one, so that by when the
last name Head was changed to Jefferies there was an engine not
unlike it, with boiler-mounted pump, built-up crank, inside-
the-footplate gear shift lh steering handle, and a seat for the man
there. These escaped the subsequent modifications performed on
the Clayton and as a result were regarded as better engines. Large
of boiler, they rarely primed, and when later fitted with the 'upside
down' Gardener governors were most economical. There was a
deadness to the crank, which had to be reverse-levered or hand-
pulled into a 'just-right' position before it would respond to the
regulator and a small man had to stretch to reach the far-back
steering wheel (still with curved spokes, although the flywheel now
had them straight) unless he let go of the high straight-up regulator;
which was not a bad habit to encourage. Steering can always wait
until she's going! The four slide-bars for the crosshead were retained
except on the last few, which had the better-looking trunk-guides.
Compounds had valves outside, some with steam-wagon type double-
high auxiliary. Like Marshalls, road locos were few and an adapta-
tion of the traction; and the chimney too had a Marshall look, small
of taper and with little flair to the deep-down brass top. (Fletcher

had been at Marshalls at one time, but there were no other like-nesses.) Drivers liked the Ransome well enough, even if it was a bit-of-a-handful and rear-heavy.

There was a good 7-ton tractor rather late in the day to sell well and an attempt at an originally boilered overtype wagon.

The firm's many other products—threshing machines, ploughs, implements and lawn mowers—diluted their interest in steam.

Robey & Co

The smallest of the four Lincoln engine makers, Robeys specialised in large portables and colliery winding engines. There were some odd-looking early tractions, with close-set-together front wheels and a few Box Patents jack-shaft models like Fowell's, before they settled down to fourshafts. These seemed rather too compact, with extremely short connections, so that rivals' drivers in the city were wont to refer to them as 'All cluttered up together on top, like a heap of muck'. Yet many users preferred them to Rustons or Claytons. They were lh steered with Pickering governors and the compounds had valves-on-top. There were traction type rollers too, but rarely seen.

Robeys made a threeshaft 5-ton tractor and very late in the day a steam-wagon type something like the Foden 'D' but with larger wheels. Earlier with steam wagons than Ransomes they had a small market which the other lacked and so the later models, by arrange-ment with Ransomes, embodied many of the features these had developed and perhaps too early discarded. This was a handsome vehicle with the set-back fronts which never looked ill on a wagon, rh steering and a 'silver' chimney top.

Another development from the wagon was a tandem steam roller, chain driven to the rear roll, popular for the newer road surfaces and long seen in use after others powered by steam had become extinct. One customer even modified this to a tri-roll by an extra connecting chain, for super-smooth surfaces.

Ruston & Proctor

This was the largest Lincoln firm, and also did not give priority to tractions, although early in the steam field with portables. Their later fourshaft engines were said to be a 'Cross between a Foster and a Clayton with the heavy rear of the former and priming propensities of the latter.' They steered on the left; had a large number of notches on the reversing quadrant instead of the usual three at either end; a boiler mounted pump; were early with Pickering governors; handled well, providing the water was low; and were handsome and well engineered, spare parts fitting at first go.

Compounds had valves-on-the-top until the merger with Hornsby, when they were then on the sides. Their 'Lincoln Imp' tractor, like McLaren's, was a fourshaft but with lh steering. Designed for government use in World War I, few were made afterwards.

Ruston rollers were not remarkable until the late twenties when they brought out a new one with rear entrance; piston valves; a tiny flywheel for quick reversing and a pump driven off the crosshead. The crankshaft pinions were always in-mesh with the second shaft's which ran loose on it in neutral, turning it when a sliding clutch, splined to the shaft, was moved along by the gear-shift lever into top or bottom. There were singles and compounds in 6 and 8-ton features. The smokebox was cast, a sensible arrangement oddly discarded by some other makers for rolled plate—which corroded at the base and burned at the sides.

Aveling-Barford, the successors of Aveling & Porter, brought this roller back to life ten years later for a special order when they were only tooled for diesels. It was put out to a sub-contractor and the exercise resumed for a time after World War II, and so the Ruston, still retaining its own brass chimney top, and with but a suggestion of Aveling in the front, was the last steam roller made.

William Tasker

Portable engines and threshing machines were the main mid-nineteenth century product, with a double cylindered traction soon following, where the steersman sat ahead of the chimney. Later there were engines on more familiar lines, but not enough of them to get known. The firm was early with tractors, beginning with a small single cylinder one known as 'The Little Giant'. Five-ton compounds followed with valves on top, the first sloping as on Fowlers and later ones flat for easier maintenance.

When tractor weight restrictions were lifted to $7\frac{1}{2}$ tons Taskers made a new one—not so soon as Garrett's, nor so numerous—but drivers liked them even better. These were original in having a chain drive from countershaft to back-axle, and links up for going forward, which retained the open rods of a threeshaft, where the flywheel 'went away from you', or anti-clockwise from the near side, as the chain-drive made the motion go in the fourshaft's direction.

It was the impression, from the drawing board, that open rods gave more efficient steam distribution than crossed ones, and makers who remained with threeshafts would sometimes say that this was a part reason for doing so. Overcoming it on motion which went the other way round by having links up, somehow did not look right, besides it being slightly harder to push 'em up than pull 'em up (with the reverse lever). Practice failed to reveal any difference between open or crossed rods on slide-valve tractions, possibly because there was not a long enough valve travel. Incidentally, piston valves with inside admission were opposite, with open rods and links down for a fourshaft's forward direction.

In its latest side-valve version this new 'Little Giant' had the steam wagon's double-high for changing the low pressure cylinder into a high pressure one when required, where other tractors merely had the knob to give a jerk of hp into it, with no separate exhaust port opening. There was a symmetry largely denied its rivals, again suggesting that what looked just right would be just right, and users were not disappointed; it was a splendid steamer, easy to handle and 'strong as they come'. A Tasker's approach was sometimes so quiet that the unexpected sight of its perky sharp flared copper topped chimney (in those traffic-free days) was sometimes startling.

There was also a larger gear driven version, more like a 5nhp traction; perhaps threshing was in mind for this, but the time was the twenties, when there were few buyers. Both could be converted to steam rollers, so that the one unit could haul stone in the summer and roll it in in the winter. But road construction was not done like this anymore; steam wagons and petrol lorries were doing the hauling, and there was more rolling in the summer than in the winter.

(On the matter of double-highs and compound knobs, 'good drivers' would take a pride in never using them, and 'bad drivers' used them too much and caused the tubes to leak. But they were there for a purpose. When manoeuvring and coupling up, the slower the revs the better, and a pull-out of the double-high extra exhaust lever and reverse movement of the regulator was then the right way; and it could also be a godsend to get over the crest of a hill. The best use for the knob was for a start when the hp crank was off-centre, followed by an immediate regulator opening. The load behind will not then snatch; also, with a bit of on-and-off, this too could be used to top a rise.)

Wallis & Steevens

Engines from this firm, like Burrell's, were always threeshafts with lh steering, but unlike them did not change the top gear pinion's

118   THE COMPLEAT TRACTION ENGINEMAN

position around at a later date, this always remaining furthest out, with the low gear next to the bearing; and there were two levers to change gear instead of one with different fulcrums, and always slipper bars for the crosshead.

There were a few compound road engines, some in showman's form, and, for a time, threshing machines not unlike Clayton's, but the speciality was agricultural traction engines, while these were in vogue. These were rather less finely made and were lower geared than most, with small straight backed bunkers, in single, compound and expansion gear form.

The first compounds had valves-on-top, 'Fowlerwise', and later ones on the sides. The fact that Wallis, then ultra conservative, made this change lends weight to the view that valves-on-the-sides was preferable, in spite of the top ones ensuring drier steam and the cranks being nearer the bearings. No doubt the steam chest for this was cheaper to make and certainly maintenance was easier; and emphasis is added by the fact that no maker ever changed over from side-valves to valves-on-top, unless indeed to special order (as on a late Ransomes or two).

The success of Burrell's single-crank-compound stimulated the adoption of expansion gear, never used before on a traction engine. There was a single cylinder, with two overlapping valves, each with its set of link motions. When on belt work the large cross-arm governor controlled the outer valve's travel by lifting the link die and so giving improved expansion without throttling the exhaust outlet, looked after by the inner valve. In good order this plan was more economical than a single, but keeping it that way was not easy with indifferent water supplies, when a valve surface is prone to score, and especially when priming. With two valves close together the scoring was doubled, thus after a relatively short period, initial economy was lost until the valves were refaced. On the road the governor was uncoupled and a lever next to the regulator then controlled the link, and the idea was to use this as an alternative regulator, with the main one left open. On a long journey, perhaps: but the method lacked precision, so most drivers left this fastened wide open with its thumb-screw and used the ordinary regulator.

When the link dies wore the timing became out of phase and steam could become trapped in the cylinder head and compressed above working pressure. This, on at least two recorded occasions has blown the end plate right out, shattering it as it did so. There would seem to have been a case for a snifter valve here to ease the pressure.

There were also Wallis tractors and wagons with enclosed motions running in an oil bath. But drivers of the day liked to see what was going on, and too often left the motion's cover open, and so got more oil on themselves than went into the bearings.

Single and compound rollers closely followed traction design with a less massive headstock than the Aveling and Fowler squares and Marshall rounds. Then in the early twenties came the revolutionary 'Advance', where the firm were both far seeing and fortunate. Recognising that an ordinary roller with its 17in wide wheels was too rear heavy for the new road surfaces, they had a complete redesign with only the shallow pleasantly-shaped copper chimney top denoting its origin. The diameter of the rear wheels was decreased and the width increased to 22in or 24in according to machine size, so both lessening and spreading the weight there. Each was separately driven and revolved on a dead axle hinged in the middle, so as to allow the wheels to fit the camber of the road instead of cutting into it. There was no flywheel, with kinetic energy to brake-off before reversing, and two high pressure cylinders—outside on disk cranks— avoided a dead centre. Thus there was no risk of a pause when reversing, which could cause a depression on black-top surfaces. The idea came from the steam winch, then seen on cranes and deck machinery. Entrance was from the rear and bunkers were at the sides. Steering was by bevel through the front roll's stalk which extended through the head, hence there was no slack, as with chains.

Besides specialist work this roller could put down hard core and scarify as well as any other. In spite of the times still being conventional, traction-engine-wise, with little development seen in half a century, the 'Advance' soon made headway and other manufacturers had to look to their laurels for a short time. Thus were Rustons stimulated, and Marshalls brought out their not dissimilar 'Universal' and they and Aveling tandems too. Yet Wallis sales remained ahead.

There was another go at a tractor, a $7\frac{1}{2}$-tonner, in 1928, following a second revision of the weight limit, but only three were made.

Miscellaneous Firms

Thos Green, Leeds were soon after Aveling with an early steam roller but never gave the impression of trying hard in this field. Later there were Green tractors, both single and compound and rollers on similar lines, the compounds having outside valves and disk crank between the big-ends. They also made garden rollers and lawn mowers, which could have diluted their interest in steam.

F. Savage, St Nicholas Works, King's Lynn made a few tractions for the same type of country as did Fowells, with a similar pinion insertion to give an extra lower gear. They were ugly little engines with set-back fronts and large 'umbrella' governors. There was also an odd-looking showman which could be used for the centre engine for their roundabout as well as for hauling, and latterly there were some better-looking tractions. Their main products were showman's equipment, including a special roundabout centre engine, a small double cylinder semi-portable with a single vertical engine on top of the smokebox for the organ and the smoke coming out underneath and led into the roundabout's hollow axle also serving [as a chimney.

Davy Paxman of Colchester had William Fletcher to design the few tractions they made, which were curiously unlike his Claytons and Ransomes in being 'wet runners'.

Goode of Royston converted Fowler single ploughing engines to tandem compounds by adding a low pressure cylinder at the end and extending the piston and valve rods to it, the chimney being moved forward to make room.

Dodman; Fisons; The Wantage Engineering Co and Brown & May, Devizes all made a few agricultural traction engines and the latter a handsome outside-valve small compound road engine as well.

John Allen, Cowley, Oxford, first known as The Oxford Steam Ploughing Co, rebuilt Fowler singles with features of their own design. They began with a boiler of greater size and pressure in the early 1900s for their own ploughing engines' replacements. The mark of a rebuild was a special chimney something after the Great Western Railway engines of the day. This tapered a little before curving out again to merge into the flared top, and was ornate, rough cast, and heavy, but a good idea, as singles played havoc with the 1/8in plate chimney (riveted along the back seam and with a half-round iron ring on top).

Allens marketed this replacement 'kit' for other steam plough owners to fit themselves, and so bring their engines to equal the lasting power on a pull with the new Fowler compounds, then beginning to compete, despite their great cost.

From this followed the Allen Ploughing Engine proper, which differed little until the compound of 1914, which had valves-on-top, trunk guides for the crossheads and retained the back-hand steerage and top-change to the vertical shaft. There were two sets of these, for the firm's own use. In 1920 a piston valve single came out, claimed to be as powerful and economical as a compound. It would pull well when 'reigned up', due to a long valve travel, and large exhaust pipes came from each end of its left-hand cylinder to join a common one which led into the side of the smokebox. The crank was balanced; the reverse lever shortened like the latest Fowler's; and the rope drum engagement altered to the clutch-on-the-vertical-shaft. The first grew out of an Allen slide-valve model sent back for conversion by a customer, so he could use it on the up-hill pulls and the hard working end of a mole drainer; the other (the right-hand engine) stayed in the set with its slide-valve, top change, long reverse lever and unbalanced big-end (and what jealousy it caused!). There were only two others, which made up a set which was sold.

Allens took their pattern for these particular engines from a Fowler design of 1860, which had 'open rods' with links up for running forward, and monkey tail regulators. If there had been any discernible improvement from open rods one would have thought the piston-valve model would have had its links down for ahead—but it retained the up position, which meant that the rods were here crossed. Drivers of these engines, in an attempt to clear their minds, have been known to change the rods over, thus crossing them for the slide-valve engine and opening them for the piston-valve one, but could detect no difference in performance in either, and of course there was an 'unnaturalness' in a lever which had to be 'back' for going forwards. (Incidentally, Marshall's Universal Roller had its short lever arranged this way.)

Armstrong Whitworth once 'lowered their sights' for a brief adventure into steam rollers. These resembled Aveling compounds of the early twenties, only were uglier in front, used a lot of fuel and did not pull. When they gave up, John Allens and Price's of Manchester shared the unsold rollers, spares and patterns, when the former soon modified the valve-gear to make their performance normal. They had a cast-iron chimney top not unlike those on the Lancashire & Yorkshire Railway (as did some Fosters) which Allens later used as a replacement for the iron ring on all their rollers chimney. (They had a large fleet of rollers, mostly Avelings and Fowlers with a sprinkling of converted Garrett tractors having the new fore-and-aft holding fork in front.)

11 Threshing Machines

Those with an interest in traction engines should not be denied an acquaintance with the threshing machine, variously known as The Machine; The Drum; The Box; The Thresher; and (in Scotland) The Mill. Engines would not have developed as they did without it—indeed the need for a self-moving engine inspired it—nor would they have lasted so long. Some of the finest drivers shared their interest with the threshing machine, many staying with it after engines had gone, once the replacing diesel-tractors-with-winches were found to make life a deal easier.

Richard Garrett was probably the first manufacturer of any size, and the only one to spell it with an 'e', as here: elsewhere there was an 'a'. Subsequently nearly all the engine makers advertised them at one time or another, including Humphreys of Pershore and Barrow & Stewart of Banbury, who only made portables (the latter's with the flywheel the firebox end). In addition there were Scottish makers, Garvie and Creighton among others.

The largest was Marshall, Sons & Co, followed closely by Clayton & Shuttleworth. Then came Ransomes, Sims & Jefferies; Ruston & Proctor; William Foster; Richard Garrett and Humphreys, with Burrell, Robey and Wallis & Steevens trailing well behind by the early 1900s and others, excepting the Scottish ones discontinuing soon after, the latter being rarely seen South. Reminders of past makers could occasionally be enlivened by finding a machine with its 'innards' removed and smooth-roofed, in Shepherd's hut form.

After the early twenties, one did not see many Garretts, and when Rustons became Ruston-Hornsby they gradually dropped out too, directing customers to Ransomes, which had the same board of directors and who were also then making the famous Ruston Clover Huller, but with four shakers instead of six, and with their own name on. Ransomes and Ruston threshers were in many ways similar, with the former the better liked.

THE "MAMMOTH" GARRETT THRESHER

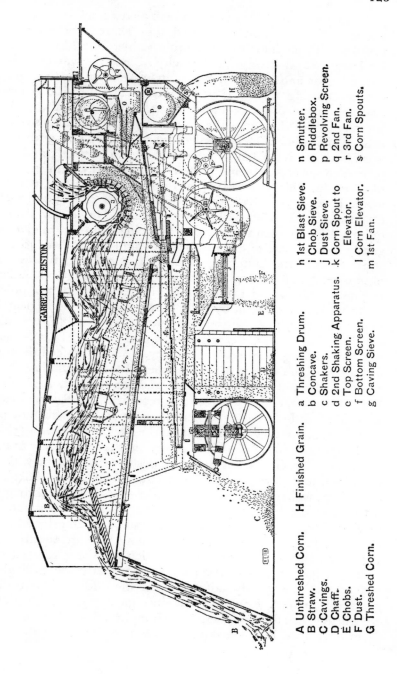

A Unthreshed Corn.
B Straw.
C Cavings.
D Chaff.
E Chobs.
F Dust.
G Threshed Corn.

H Finished Grain.

a Threshing Drum.
b Concave.
c Shakers.
d 2nd Shaking Apparatus.
e Top Screen.
f Bottom Screen.
g Caving Sieve.

h 1st Blast Sieve.
i Chob Sieve.
j Dust Sieve.
k Corn Spout to Elevator.
l Corn Elevator.
m 1st Fan.

n Smutter.
o Riddlebox.
p Revolving Screen.
q 2nd Fan.
r 3rd Fan.
s Corn Spouts.

Although all threshers came to look alike, users found there were many differences, and some held they shared the same characteristics with engines from the same stable. The Marshall engine, for instance was handy but 'snatchy'. Similarly was the Marshall 'Drum' neat and compact, but snatchy with its sheaves, grabbing and swallowing whole, if you weren't careful, with generally a 'thump' unless properly thinned out. The feeder always had to 'watch-out' lest he cause the engine down below to lose its even beat. This rather ill-mannered drum would try and grab what he was about to give it before he was ready, so to speak, and when it succeeded the engine would protest and bark away until its governors lifted again. This, particularly if it was also a Marshall, when there would be a very emphatic CHAFF-chuff ; CHAFF-chuff ; CHAFF-chuff ; CHAFF-chuff before it settled down again. The Foster drum had quite a different character, taking anything you liked to give it, and gently too. Its feeder did not have to spin-out a sheaf to the last straw to keep the humming—and what a rich one it was—on an even note. And if the engine were also a Foster—a smooth and gentle engine by the way—its recovery from a good old 'bump' down the drum would be sluggish by comparison and you'd only hear 'kerr-PHUT; kerr-PHUT; kerr-PHUT; kerr-PHUT; kerr-PHUT' (Fosters usually chuffed 'backwards,' emphasising the second beat). Clayton machines were gentle too, but choosey. You had to feed them right, or they wouldn't take it, and an unopened sheaf would just sh-sh-sh-sh-sh on the top until lifted back and fanned out. And, like the Clayton engine, there were constant modifications. Ruston machines were liked little better than Ruston engines. They did not prime, of course ... but they did bung so, at the back of the cavings riddle—the long one at the end. This oscillated on the same throw as the top shoe, above it, instead of in the opposite direction, as with other machines, and thus gave little encouragement to the short straws, or cavings, which fell through the shaker-slats to shuffle through, and then off in the opposite direction. (The top shoe was a backwards sloping slide, and the caving riddle was stepped, and sloped towards the outlet.) A part-cure here was to remove the yard-square inspecting door half way along the shoe, which was for getting at shaker bearings, letting a proportion of the material come through here instead, but falling only half-way along the riddle, where it did not get sifted so well. Ransome machines gave every satisfaction but were heavy, like their engines. And Humphreys'—well, some thought them developed little since portable engine times. Yet they lasted, and many sophisticated East Anglians (threshing-wise) liked them. It may have been because the sometimes closed-in, almost humless, octagonal drum with concave-like bars across it instead of the normal open serated beater-bars was gentler with barleys; and the long stroke of the slow moving shoes (shoes 'framed' the riddles) did mean less bunging with barley-awns in the bottom sieve. There was a time when Humphreys' held that machines with this type of drum were safer than an ordinary one, as being less likely to come apart through centrifugal force. But other makers ignored this risk and stuck to their open ones.

There was a long period when threshing machines tended to be more popular near their place of origin, but as knowledge spread, Marshalls, Fosters and Ransomes began to stand out from among the rest. Claytons were unfortunate in closing their works down in the late twenties, when there was still a long life ahead for this product. With the coming of rubber tyres to tractors there was an expanding farmers' market as well as that of the threshing contractor, then turning to tractors also. Marshalls acquired the threshing-machine-side of Clayton & Shuttleworth, but were slow in adopting features of the rather better Clayton machine; its 'gentleness' and more efficient barley-awner only appearing in their last steel-framed models (blamed for weight, but matured-timber was hard to come-by then).

The best feature of a Marshall was the third-blower. Properly handled it gave a better sample, particularly with oats, where it could blow out the blind ones (those with nothing in 'em). The Foster, popular in wheat-growing Lincolnshire, had longer shakers than a Marshall; an advantage and particularly so when positioned a little head-down. Most makers had various sizes in the standard 4ft 6in range besides the rare 5ft and the 4ft and smaller ones. Fosters tended to be lighter size-for-size and had larger sieves. They doubtless thought Lincs farmers did not grow enough 'rubbish' to warrant a third blower and that the value in stressing simplicity was that there were less gadgets to go wrong. Certainly a third blower left full-on would put good corn into the 'rubbish' bag. The Ransome machine equalled the Foster in sieves and shakers, was better finished, and because of its greater weight, stood better at work. It took more lugging around, though: a disadvantage on heavy going.

The order of bags were two on the right, used alternatively for the best corn with a shutter to change them over. Most of the corn came through to these inside the adjustable wire screen by an auger,

which also adjusted telescopically with it. The next (middle) bag
was for the thin 'tail' corn, which came through the wires; and the
left-one where small seeds and dust which escaped the top fan fell
through. Marshalls third blower fanned the material before it reached
the screen and the flap on its air-intake was adjusted by a thumb-
screw in a curved slide near it, on the outside.

The average weight of a threshing machine was $4\frac{3}{4}$-tons and most
machines had four shakers carried on two crankshafts and a main
winnower ('Bottom Blower') driven from the drum shaft at a rather
slower speed (the drum 'hummed' round at 1,000 to 1,100rpm, its
8in pulley driven by a 60ft 6in belt from the engine's usually 4ft 6in
flywheel, and this thus going at about 160rpm, in a pleasant double
'chuffing' rhythm). Also from a small pulley on the main shaft a
crossed belt went straight along to the shakers' ('Walkers' running
from the drum to the far-end) second crankshaft, where a 20in
pulley turned it at 180rpm. A straight belt ran back and lower to
the riddles' (or shoes') four-throw crankshaft with a centre bearing, which went at 220rpm, or so, varying with make and model.
Also from the main shaft, generally on the rh, back and horizontal,
was a belt driving the awner pulley at drum speed. (Marshall's
third blower was a fan on the far end of the awner shaft.) The top
fan, above the sackman's head, was driven by an inside pulley on
the awner shaft; and off the riddle crankshaft on the near-side was a
small pulley for the slow moving screen, and a similar one the other
side for the corn elevator. This had a buckle on it to vary its length
when the cup elevators' belt needed tightening, done by sliding the
top shaft further away by long bolts—a common way of belt-
tightening. The other belts had Crocodile, or Jacksons' fasteners, so
that pieces could be taken out when they stretched, or short lengths
added when they started to come apart at the fastener ends, with
weathering and wear and tear. The top blower went faster than
drum speed and could send a powerful blast between the two sieves
(generally distinguished from 'riddles' by being smaller) there which
moved with the top shoe, and received corn as it fell from the awner.
Blowers are regulated by shutters at each side, and if left too far
open on this one, light grains, like oats, blew back into the machine
and went through again, overloading and blocking the corn elevator:
a not infrequent happening when a regular driver was away; or with
a farmer's machine.

The humming was most noticeable at the straw-end, varying in
pitch with each shaker revolution, so that, particularly with a

Foster, the drum seemed to be saying 'More-more-more-more-m-m-m-m-more-more,' the top of the machine rocking a little, meanwhile, as if keeping time, which increased a few seconds every minute or two when the faster riddle cranks caught up with the shakers' and synchronized. Superimposed was a clicking from the awner and blowers' belts as their fasteners raced over the pulleys, and often too would be a 'clobber-clobber-clobber' from the riddle cranks, their wooden connecting 'rods' going forward, an outside and an inside opposed pair to oscillate the top and bottom shoes, sloped to move the grain to their ends and holding frames above, into which the sieves slid, varying in hole-size according to the crop. The shoes were suspended by $2\frac{1}{2}$in wooden slats on the outside of the machine, holding-lugs for them coming through slots on the sides.

Threshing began by the handcutter picking up a sheaf, from where it had been fork-placed on the top, with the flat of his curved serated knife, swinging it across, butt-end first, to the feeder and twisting his wrist, so that the string band was cut. He would sometimes pull out the string with his other hand, but more usually only when he cut near a knot, which made for tidier string-handfulls, as straws adhered otherwise. The feeder usually in the 'feeding hole', the engine side of the drum, the same width and about a foot deep, would then dribble the sheaf over its whizzing heaters, which were low enough down not to get his arm in unless he was very careless—and even then protection was afforded by the drum lid, designed to close the aperture when leaned-forward-on. He fed from his receiving arm, assisted by flicks of his free hand. Practice could result in the material going into the drum in one continuous slither, so that the engine below had a steady and regular load and the fans and riddles would not have their motion varied. The knack was keeping a little in the other hand, dribbling in, when leaning over towards the bandcutter for the next sheaf. Usually, wheat was fed straight across; oats on the slant; and barley straight down.

The beaters knocked the grain out against the concave bars spaced 6in straight across and square-edged with thick wires threaded through them. The concave went about a third of the way round the drum and for most crops was adjusted to $1\frac{1}{2}$in away from the drum at the top; $\frac{1}{2}$in in the middle and $\frac{1}{4}$in or less at the bottom. Most of the grain went through the concave and then jostled forward on the sloping shoe towards the back of the cavings riddle, where the few short straws with it joined the fall-out mentioned as often troubling a Ruston thresher.

The threshed straw's momentum then zipped it ahead onto the shakers (or walkers) which tossed it along 15ft or so to the outlet, and grains left among it were then shaken out through their slats to joint the cavings, meeting those which had gone through the concave wires. Two sets of baffle plates with swinging flaps adjusted by chains from the top prevented high velocity grains which had gone round with the beater bars from shooting out like bullets over the top of the straw.

Underneath the stepped cavings riddle, the slope was the reversed, and the outlet back towards the centre. Grain shuffling through this met a blast of air from the bottom blower, which sent most of the chaff mixed with it ahead and underneath. This could be directed sideways as an alternative, but then needed more frequent raking away, lest the spout for it bung up. The bottom sieve caught and spread the grain-flow and let it fall through. The elevator's cups here took over and conveyed the grain to the top again, while thistle heads, chibbled straws and the like came over the top to form a small heap on the ground.

From the cups, it fell into an auger on the awner-shaft which led into the awner proper, a cylinder with a sloping ribbed interior, where the first part was razor-blade-shaped but blunt, cast-iron pieces on the shaft, and angled to pass the grain along. This chopped most of the awns off barley and rubbed off white-heads (husks) left on wheat, and then released the contents through a small swinging door at its base, which was usually enough for barleys, as malting samples were more likely to germinate when a few awns were on here and there. But with the door clamped shut, the second part of the awner, four upended bars, a little on the 'skew', could complete the final 'polishing'—with some risk of a bung, withall. To avoid the awner, with oats or wet corn, there was a slide-opening underneath the auger, moved by a push and pull handle outside. Pulling this out when the awner belt was 'whistling' (the noise of slipping) did not always prevent it coming off through a bung when wet corn was on the blades. When the atmosphere was damp, dust over this opening would solidify, and seeds there start to grow and reinforce it into a pad. Thus did the slide-hole have to be kept clear, which was one of the 'jobs around the tackle'. From here, as mentioned, there was a second winnowing and sieving before reaching the grading screen.

A foible of some farmers was to request that the screen be opened to take out more tail corn, and soon after, say that this was done too much and it must be closed a little. To do this the adjusting handle was pushed into its square at the shaft's end outside and held still, while the screen's going round would do the unwinding and so extend the spaces between the coiled wires. (On these, here and there, would be a soldered clasp to hold the light-metal augur inside, which opened and shut with it.) When the farmer said 'Enough' the handle would be slipped off, and if he said 'too much' the screen had to be wound up again. This was less simple and could only be done at the next meal break. First it had to be opened fully, and banged with fists to shake out as many grains as possible from between the wires. Then there was a little screwing up and laborious 'pickle outs' with the tang-end of a file or old knife each time to get out every grain, lest the wires bend with the tightening. This could use up a whole meal-time. Thus a reaction of some drivers was to disconnect the squared bit from the screw, so that when the handle was held on it, nothing happened. As long as the farmer thought it was opening, which he generally did—one had to know one's man of course—this was all right. The pantomime of closing, with much useless hand winding was also played after a 'Too much'!

Screens gave less trouble and much time was saved, when they were left alone after being once adjusted to let a token amount of tail corn and splits trickle through, and it was surprising what good samples came from this near-enough method.

Sacking-off was generally the wagoners job and required strength, skill and balance. A sack of wheat weighed 2½cwt; barley 2cwt; and oats about 1¾cwt. The latter came off quickest, and so were just as hard work. Bags were hotched or dragged from their shutes to a weighing machine, then to a lifter, wound up to shoulder height and carried to a near-by cart, or, sometimes with oats, up barn steps to be emptied (or 'shot').

A youth would take the chaff away in a large wicker basket and periodically pull out the cavings. Neglect would cause blockages, so the driver's eye was often on him.

The straw generally fell into an elevator. Early on, and nearly always in East Anglia these were single-troughed Hayes types 22ft or 24ft long with the returning rakes coming back over the top. Thus wind was of little bother and the straw rick could be built close-up to them. But they were too short for much more than a day's threshing at a setting. Thus in other parts both folding, and telescopic 30ft and longer elevators were used. Here the rakes returned under-neath—and side winds could blow the straw out of the trough! There was much handle-winding on the fold or unfold (or slide in and slide out, as the case may be). But this type could put up larger stacks and would also work at an angle of up to 60 degrees. The elevator belt came off a 4in pulley on the end-shaker-shaft and ran crossed over jockey-pulleys-on-angle-irons, for an angled set. The belt was made up of buckle-jointed lengths as there were many variations required in length between straight going and the varying angles. Such adjustments could be done when threshing, as the belt was very slow running and could be pulled off or pressed back easily enough, the heap of straw mounting up in the elevator base-trough not mattering much as long as the thresher's shakers were clear. The slower an elevator ran, providing it could get the straw away the better, so sometimes a smaller shaker-shaft-pulley would be carried for the lighter crops.

The straw-rick men, seldom more than two, were often elderly, for the work was light and experience essential. The 'server' would let the straw heap up as it dropped from the elevator and then pass on a downwards slope to the 'builder', who carefully placed each forkful and trod it in. (Their forks had two prongs with handles varying from 5ft to 6ft). When the wind was behind the engine, which the driver liked, keeping him out of the dust, these men got most of the smoke, and loud then could be their vociferations!

An experienced corn rick team, two or three in number could establish a rhythm. The first would 'follow the courses,' picking each sheaf cut to a set time, and if he missed or could not see one soon enough he'd swing his fork empty. The next would follow his motions, and if the rick was getting low, pass up-hill to the pitcher, who stood on an eminence of sheafs lifting up and over his head to the bandcutter. If a sheaf was not flicked round to land butt-end first to this man—a little slant was overlooked—it could sometimes appear back on the rick as the pitcher was turning away for the next one! But he too could have his grievance if the bandcutter, to 'save his back', kept the same pile in front of him which be began with when the rick was higher.

Should wheat straw be required for thatching, if it was long and clean enough, the more straight across it went the better, as thatching straw should not be bent or broken, which 'going in' at an angle did to it. At such times the feeder would 'fork feed,' first filling his feed-hole and then building a slide for the bandcutter to drop the cut sheaves on. From this he would rake downward with reversed fork, keeping a little on the tines with a twist of the wrist for dribbling down until the next one was before him. A skilled feeder could also fork-feed barley and oats as smoothly as by hand. The sheaf would be picked off the slide with a little preliminary spill, and then, a shake and twist could make it fan out, full width of the drum, to go down 'slicewise'.

When any threshed barley heads appeared in the cavings the driver would have some straw put on the top and at the next meal-time the feeder pushed this down to wedge behind the top half of the concave. This was called 'stuffing the breast,' and stopped the trouble but treated the grains more severely, so that it was sometimes better that they by-passed the awner.

For horse-beans (hard and black) the safety attachment came off the feeding place; the top half of the concave's adjusting rod was drawn out, letting it fall away from the beaters, and a shaped metal blank hooked over and bolted back, with a tie-washer behind. The middle and bottom adjustments were opened, sieves changed for those with the largest holes, blowers opened full, and awner handle pulled out. Hurdles covered with an old tarpaulin would then make a tent over the drum, and this be run at a lower speed. Beans were easily shelled and the object was not to crack them with too much beater-speed and yet have enough to blow as much of their heavy chaff out as possible. It was not an easy compromise, but as beans were not a frequent chore for the threshermen, preferable to removing every other beater-bar to permit full speed, as recommended in the instruction books. (Getting them back again would not have been easy, as beaters had to be balanced.)

Here feeder and handcutter could stand face-to-face, each with a knife if one of them was, or could work, left-handed. The sheaves were thrown direct onto the drum, which, being 'open' did its own feeding, in a rough sort of way. They had to go straight across to prevent the stiff black stalks from lodging. When they did this, the feeder would seize his fork, and with careful movements, straighten them out. A learner trying it, could lose a fork down the drum, often bending a concave bar or two as it went. The tent was to keep the beans from flying all over the place, and did not always prevent a few nasty smacks in the face, although its frame of hurdles was comforting for a man to grasp when a little off balance. The noise, especially alongside a Dutch barn, was impressive, the open un-shrouded top un-muffling it so to speak, and the larger sheaves would crash through the beaters like breakers booming on rocks. If the wind was towards the engine the coarse black dust would put a coat of fur on it and little heaps build up at each end of the crosshead's slide (as it did with clover-rubbing). Dust building up on the beater bars after a period of bean threshing and also when bunged with thistle-downs, with barley. This could be 'whizzed off' and after a meal break by putting the engine's reverse lever over and turning the machine momentarily backwards.

The feeder was the driver's mate and relieved by him about 10am and 3pm for an hour's break to 'crack some coal, clean brasses and keep his eyes open'—although some of the older drivers with a competent mate would occasionally stay up 'on top' feeding themselves most of the day. Feeding could develop into a waking dream, particularly with clean barley, where a man could lean back, cushioned with sheaves, and with a minimum of hand movement and a little swaying, flick one after another—and another—and another—to slither down the drum, thin as paper, and soon to be filling the elevator with their yellow straw. All around would be the 'Hum-m-m-humm-m-mmm-mm-mm,' not too loud, felt as well as heard, while dust would lightly settle on eyelashes and around nose and mouth and be left to stay there. Blowing noses, wiping faces and swearing at the discomfort were for the not-used-to-it farmer's men. If the handcutter was one of these he would have to arrange his own time away for a smoke. But if a 'follower,' (a casual hand) an engineman would cut-bands-and-feed at certain times so that he could 'go and get some of the dust out of him'.

Before the turn of the century threshing machines had plain wick-fed brass bearings which were filled with oil twice a day—the back shaker-cranks' outside ones; the non-pulley side of the riddle crank and the blowers, without any danger while the wheels were turning. The remaining outside ones and the riddle-shaft's big-ends and centre bearing were 'before a start' and 'midday' tasks. The mate oiled the shakers' inside bearings which meant an uncomfortable crawl along the slats. And as engines did not then have oil-pumps, the brass displacement lubricators on the cylinder and over the slide valve also had to be filled several times a day with warmed cylinder oil through their tiny apertures. What with these things, the odd belt repairs and continually walking round to see that everything was running properly, a driver could be kept fully occupied. This did not apply to all, though: some would sit on their engine and smoke for very long periods. These were the ones 'with no ear for music' and whose omissions had a habit of building-up on them in frequent stoppages, heavy repairs and eventual loss of trade.

Ring-oilers, where a loose ring ran round the shaft conveying oil from a larger sump, and more positively than a wick, followed plain bearings on the outside. Their once-a-week top-up saved much time. The slow moving screen and corn elevator bearings depended on the oil can, but not very often. Ring-oilers had to be watched, however, when their felt retaining washers leaked.

A real break-through came with ball-bearings all over, optional (and strangely, not always stipulated) by the mid-twenties, and standard thenceforth. As oil pumps too were on most engines by then it could be thought that drivers had an easier time. But as so often happens with 'improvements', the reverse was more often the case. No longer was he a pampered man, with a can of the farmer's beer near by: even tea was rare. Times were hard in the farming world and casual labour pared down. A driver who did not lend-a-hand on the rick as it got lower, or aid with the sacks, could be made to feel he would not be invited to thresh there again.

The early way of keeping a thresher still was by chain blocks. These were hung over the back axle when travelling for easy reach when setting. They were 4–5in wide, joined by a chain at either end and sloped where they faced each other. The 'away' piece would be pulled tight to its wheel and the chains adjusted so that a wedge could be hammered between the opposite piece and the wheel's iron tyre with a sledge or the iron bar's blunt end—another accessory, the iron bar. A wheel lying low would be jacked-up and the wedge placed sufficiently under it until the back-spirit-level's bubble was near enough to centre. The sides' spirit levels mattered less, and a little up-hill was no fault, especially with a short shakered machine.

Lever lifting chocks were a subsequent invention, less handy and stored on the cavings riddle along with the main belt and numerous other things, and so were not favoured everywhere. The 'away' block had lugs on it and the other, iron channels or ridges, which sloped from the top on its opposite end. Bars with a choice of holes went over the lugs and onto others on a heavy iron piece which fitted into the top channel, and had a slot to take the curved end of a 4ft lever, which when sloped downwards, could be bumped back against the wheel at its elbow. This action jolted the iron piece down into the next slot. A pull down with the lever then brought the blocks tightly together. Should one side require raising, the process could be continued until the blocks met. To unfasten, the lever would go into a slot on top of the block, and its elbow again bumped back against the wheel, which would gradually draw the block away.

When setting, the machine would be pushed or pulled onto long scotches in front (the lighter end) if low there, and 'packing' aimed under a low wheel behind, so that only a marginal levelling was left for the lifting-chocks. A great aid to levelling was the 'German Jack'. This was some 2ft 3in high, and heavy. A geared-down handle moved its racked lifting piece, which had a claw on top and a foot at the base. The top could go under the main chassis, the sack-end, where an iron pad was put there for it; or the foot piece could go under a wheel hub, with a piece of wood packing between to prevent its slipping out—which could give the man who was winding it a nasty blow on the head with the claw.

Bolster-blocks, near-oblongs a foot long, tapering sideways and lengthways went between the turning and still parts of the fore-carriage, tapped sideways and endways to lessen the rocking caused by the shakers.

When rubber tyres came in, makers seemed reluctant to replace the wooden and iron wheels they had used for a century, and there was little aid from them, in keeping a rubbered machine still. Necessity caused users themselves to invent back-axle stands and chassis-jacks. The stands, a little above axle-high triangles of $2\frac{1}{2}$in strip-iron on 3ft wooden bases and indented for the axle to rest in, would take the weight after a lift each side with the German Jack, a low side packed underneath or shimmed in the indenture—the other side then had to have a little scooped out underneath its wheel, or this first raised. The jacks were near chassis high tubes on foot square bases with threaded inserts going down a foot inside. These were placed as near the front as possible and screwed out a bit at a time while the machine was running, to take-up each jerk (or lift) every time the shakers' and riddles' crankshafts synchronised. A short bar through a hole at the top could do a final twitch. Only then did the machine stand firm.

When being moved in between stacks pushing was preferred to pulling, so as to keep the engine on ground which was generally drier; also awkward places in farmyards could be better negotiated with the push-pole, and the engine was then nearly in-line for the belt, too. Here, its own length back, and a little left to line-up the inside of the flywheel with the offside of the machine and the belt would go on. Perfection was a little further 'left' to allow for the pulley inside the main one on the drum (driving the 'riddle'), but as engine flywheel and drum pulley had well cambered surfaces the 60ft belt would run 6in or so on either side of this; time was often a factor when

men were waiting to start, and moving too much on wet ground to
be discouraged, thus 'near-enough' was often 'good-enough'. An
added reason for push-pulling was that the less an engine moved
about when off the hard road the fewer the wheel marks and ruts.

Push-pulling was hard work for the mate. Front axle guide chains
would be out full length to prevent the lock getting out-of-hand, and
steering then done by tugging on the drawbar, aided by whoever
stood near, and a small scotch to place under a 'forard' wheel and
kick-out now and then, thus bringing a little 'power-steerage' into
play.

The sheet had flaps back and front to cover the shaker end and
back face, and had to be tied 'just so'. Method varied with the
district, but the main thing was that the cords were in known places,
so that the man who undid them knew where they were on a dark
winter's morning. It was folded on top unless wet, when it was
spread on the ground.

The wing boards of Marshalls and Ransome machines were lifted
by their attached iron stay supports hanging on the sides and which
then fitted into a recess, when the boards were horizontal. Some
Fosters had them this way too, but with most other makes the boards
folded over the top and the mate had to have someone below to
lower them down with a separate support. Front and back end
boards were then fixed vertically and a side board, away from the
rick, joined them together. An extension was added to the rick side
which rested on foot pieces to the main wing board and its outside
suspended by short chains from the top of the end boards.

Most machines drew from the lighter shaker-end, with Fosters
offering the turntable on the corn-end as an alternative. Large
farmers sending their own machine round to their several farms
tended to favour these, as they were the more wont to have hard
stands everywhere. A driver who knew his business could then, on
hard ground, push in with his engine front on the drawbar and
control the lock with his own. Unsetting with this type was simplicity
itself, the elevator hooking on behind the shakers with little preliminary movement; the engine first hitching the two machines back
with a short chain from its front so that it could have an unobstructed
turn-round after pulling past sack-lifter, weigher and coal and corn
carts. A few Claytons were also this way and round both makes
recognised then by having corn-elevators outside the main frame.
Some of the earlier Claytons had a fan-cum-impeller in lieu of
elevator belt. This sent the grain spinning uphill through a similar

channel, but used more power and easily bunged with wet corn. Another Clayton feature was single-crank-shakers, an early design offered as an alternative until about 1915. Here there were five shakers instead of four and the crank was midway. The outside and centre shakers were supported on rocker arms in front, and the other two had them behind. This gave the non-rocking end a greater radius and thus greater vertical lift to the straw, with its neighbour having a pushing-out motion. Some thought these shakers need not be so long to do their job, but most buyers preferred the double-crank. With a single mid-way crank the belt to an elevator had to be much longer, and similarly the chain to a straw tier, when used, which then tended to sway and the more often come off. (Straw tiers were not generally loved, chaff cutters behind, positively hated, and the heavy and awkward baler only came in late in the day.) About 1912 (Clayton machines came out with a very large wheel on the riddle crankshaft, a good idea because there was less belt slip, and early identified by being partly inside the rear road wheel. Yet they reverted to one of original size later on (the ratio was kept the same on both models). Also up to about that time, Ransomes had a crossed belt to the awner. Later they changed it to the straight belt of other manufacturers. A rarely seen Ruston & Proctor aberration was eccentrics off the end-shaker to move the shoes by long connecting rods. This eliminated a riddle crankshaft, but put a double load on the shaker belt, which was prone to slip on its small drive pulley. This did show, however, that the shoes could be efficient at no more than shaker speed, providing they had long enough travel.

A long riddle-crank-throw possibly saved the Humphreys machine from extinction as there were other features which made it less popular, and when Marshalls, who should have known better, first designed their steel framed model, barley awns often blocked the bottom sieve, its travel being short and speed high. By increasing the one with bigger-throw cranks and reducing the other by using a larger pulley, there was a great improvement.

Threshing was best seen a little a-slant the rear on a still and sunny day, first at a distance enough to get it in focus, then twice as far back again, so that the dust blended with shadows on the machine's red or salmon-pink.

The 'chink-chink-chink-chink' of the chains hanging on the engine bunker would be faintly heard, and in-time with the big-end's brass lubricator-top flashing up, nearly three times a second behind the backplate above. Beyond the blur of governors, the chimney, 'smiling' if it had a brass or copper top 'to give it expression', would voice its double exhaust beat in unison as it pushed out the smoke in thick black intervals. The belt, running straight along from its hiding place below the drum's wing board to the top of the flywheel, would return underneath in dips and sways, while humming would be all round and seemingly everywhere, rising and falling; and cutting through would be the regular clink of belt fasteners and a periodic rapid one from the sack lifter's ratchet. Sometimes, there would be a voice, or a cart-horse's whinney indistinct, and losing itself in the ever persistent deep monotone with just a bit of lighter 'z-z-z-z-z-z-z-' to it now and then.

The figures of the corn rick men, bandcutter, and feeder would be moving together, their efforts seen in the elevator's crinkly dull-gold load slowly moving upwards, where smaller figures were momentarily hidden behind where it fell.

There would be an aroma too, mixing with the smoky oily engine one to form a blend, particularly delicious if the crop was barley, and fainter, but so very clean, if wheat; and, now and then, a musti-ness from damp patches. Closer at hand, a sharp sourness was often near bearings where mineral oil seeped onto the dusts from many plants, and formed a paste.

The Threshing Machine was such a part of the real Engine World and intimately known and understood by so many drivers, that it seems strange to see it should be so neglected now. Engines by them-selves are like cups without saucers; or a football game without goal posts. It's because of the Threshing Machine that the engine was born.

How lonely an agricultural traction looks when on the road today without a 'Drum' behind it; or standing in a field or farmyard with-out its mate in sight! Clean and spotless it may well be at Rallies, but just a little threshing-dust here and there, and some straws in the spud-box would not be unbecoming.

12 Sorting Them Out

The Best Threshing Engine

This type must not be too heavy yet its boiler should be large enough for good steaming, lasting power and non-priming. It should be compact, as often when threshing the bunker would be close up to a wall, to allow the machine to be mid-way along its rick, and handle well without too much stretching, and be economical with a quick response to the governors. The lock should be as short as possible yet it not be light enough in front to rear and slew, as sometimes happened when this was set-back. It is better not on springs, which add to the weight, and lessen ground clearance and also better with only one set of motions to oil, clean and adjust, as sometimes drivers suffered hunger for lack of time to eat.

Of the engines reviewed, the 7nhp agricultural singles by Allchin, Aveling, Robey, and Wallis and the 6nhp Burrell single-crank compound and Marshall 6nhp single (nearly a 7, with its 10lb more on the clock than most 6s) come within this range. The earlier Allchin, the Wallis could perhaps be eliminated, as it was not a popular engine, few being seen far from Basingstoke; nor were there many Robeys; and there must be some reason why Aveling threshing engines were so few and far between. This leaves a fairly late four-shaft Allchin with Pickering governors and left-hand steering, but not as late as Royal Chester, that most modelled of engines, which was heavier; and the Burrell and Marshall.

Imagine a threshing contractor having all three, of the same age and in good order, when even he would be 'hard put to it' to say which was the best. The Burrell and Marshall would be a shade the more economical, with the former better at threshing-and-cutting, being stronger and quieter, even if a little uneven. On ordinary threshing there would be more tube sweeping; then there would be the periodic crosshead adjustments; and the rope drum, not being free, would have to be wound out with power every time,

instead of an un-latch and pay-out, which was something to con-
sider when crossing a wet field requiring many 'pulls'. Both engines
were snatchy on the regulator, particularly the Marshall, which
could attract a hand continuously to it when shunting about, restricting the driver's movements and preventing him steering with two
hands on sticky and uneven ground. However, the Marshall would
be the more lively on the crank, although the other's could readily
be brought into a starting position by a touch of the compound knob
and a just-back-beyond-centre flick of the reverse. And its knob was
particularly useful for coupling-up, or tightening the belt under
steam, when only half a revolution, or even less, would do. The contractor might see his farmers leaning towards the Burrell, as being
the quieter and less likely to throw sparks; and drivers ever so slightly
towards the Marshall, preferring a fourshaft, yet less so if the Burrell
was a late enough one with balanced big-end, which took the jerk
out of the belt and smoothed the 'travelling slow' when chaining and
setting: but then, that rope drum!

    With the Allchin, its smaller diameter rear wheels would lessen
the back weight, so that it would cut in less; its relative shortness
would improve the lock; its being a 7nhp would give it a quieter
exhaust than the Marshall's because of the less effort, and too the
Marshall was apt to rear a little on occasions; and the 12in stroke
against the others' 10in made for as smooth going as the Burrell with
a balanced big-end, which, added to the easy non-snatchy regulator
(a push one, but no advantage here over the others' pulls) made it
the easiest to handle. Then it was one up over the Burrell with its
free rope drum. Also with the Allchin was that indefinable something, call it proportion or what you will, which looked just right,
aided by the perfect shape—not too flared, as the Burrell's just was,
not too austere like the Marshall's—of its polished chimney top.

    The owner could be frustrated by the spares for his Allchin, which
seldom fitted without alteration, and there was little advantage from
interchangeability of parts, should he have a second one. Indeed, if
his trade made him think of setting up in a big way he would plumb
for one of the other two, most likely the Marshall. Yet, taken as an
engine by itself, the Allchin would seem to win slightly on points
and enough were made over a long period to give an assurance
of their basic quality being constant.

The Best Road Locomotive

Requirements differ from a threshing engine's. Weight was no disadvantage and springs, awning, three speeds and extra water tanks
were part of the specification. Makers which continued after so
many began were Fowler, Burrell, Aveling and (mostly as showmen)
Foster, with the two first so far ahead in demonstrating customers'
preferences that the best rests between them.

Although Burrells made twice as many showmen as Fowlers, the
latter made the most, overall, and so had the greater experience. If
Burrells claimed that their threeshaft absorbed less power, Fowlers
ignored this and concentrated in having power to spare and a big
enough boiler to feed it. Burrells had the small advantage of lh
steering and their later road engines had—at last—a free rope drum.
But Fowlers changed to lh steering in their last few showman's
versions of the Lion. What did drivers think? On the whole they
tended to come down on the Fowler side, preferring the slightly
lower top gear, which made them faster with a heavy load over a
long distance as there was less changing down on hills; and its
steaming and pulling power could not be bettered. Thus one would
think the Fowler the better, but not by a great a margin.

The Best Ploughing Engine

The Fowler BB and the slightly heavier BB1 were the right size for
most English conditions; there were many more of them than
equivalent sizes of Avelings and McLarens; drivers liked them better
and the BB especially, was beautifully proportioned. As the BB1 had
a little more stamina few will contest the view that this was the best
ploughing engine.

The Best Steam Tractor

There was little to choose between any of the compound 5-tonners,
but Burrells sold the most. Later the Garrett dominated the market
and another good one after the first weight restriction was the Fowler
Tiger. Both of these have been critized for only having two speeds.
But tractors were still limited to size and so lacked sufficient boiler
capacity to make the best of a third gear, except when running
empty one way, as with timber hauling. The Clayton and the
Ransome 7-tonners were also good, but too few. None, however,
raised the same enthusiasm as the Tasker chain-drive 'Little Giant'
in its valves-on-the-sides form with solid forged crankshaft to stand

the extra load of its double-high, and there were enough made to qualify it as the best steam tractor of orthodox design.

Many of the later tractors came out new with solid rubber tyres, thus have the double advantage of improved adhesion, a quality lacking with such light-weights on metal tyres.

None of the above compared with the Foden 'D' in performance and speed, but as it was a derivative of the steam wagon, and not seen until the others had almost departed from the scene this must come within a specialist category.

The Best Steam Wagon

At all stages of its development Foden was the best. As a perfected overtype it was first in the field and was still finding customers after competitors had given up making them.

The Best Steam Roller

As has been said Aveling & Porter made more rollers than all the other manufacturers put together, although Fowlers and Marshalls did not 'play at it' either. The former tended to follow Aveling's lead, their later models having trunk guided crossheads, straight-up regulator, compactness and other non-Fowler features, although always retaining valves-on-top for compounds, which even Marshalls discarded for 'on the sides' in their piston valve ones. Marshalls kept on with, after Avelings had discarded them.

The Aveling piston-valve single of the twenties with balanced big-end and a second injector replacing the pump, in good hands, was the perfect roller (of ordinary type). As economical and smooth as a compound it had the right look about it too. But statistics at Rochester showed that good hands were scarce and that a little careless priming soon scored the valve cylinder, resulting in the carefully assessed boiler size becoming inadequate for sustained demands on it. Thus, with a sigh, it seemed, did the drawing office again get busy, resulting in new slide-valves; a geared-down pump which always went; the easiest chain steering ever, with enclosed worm-and-pinion; a compound motion so well balanced that it never 'shook itself to pieces' no matter how rough the handling; and even the regulator improved, which had always been a good feature. In spite of Wallis 'Advance' inroads, there was still a market for the orthodox, of which this was indeed the best.

The best types of machines may be summarised as follows:

Threshing engine   Allchin lh steered fourshaft with Pickering governors.

Road locomotive   Fowler 'Lion'.

Ploughing engine   Fowler BB1.

Steam wagon   Foden.

Orthodox steam tractor   Tasker 'Little Giant'.

Late-type tractor   Foden 'D'.

Orthodox roller   Aveling & Porter's latest slide-valve type.

Specialist roller   Wallis & Steevens 'Advance'.

Epilogue

Once symmetry was achieved towards the end of the last century, the traction engine came to be decorated with brass and copper, blacked here painted there, polished, pampered and loved. To many a driver it was his world, and sole topic of conversation in pub and farmyard. It could fill the minds of boys to the exclusion of too much else. To them nothing was more thrilling than the distant toll of its gearing, the approaching rattle and jingle, the smell of smoke and of steam distilled from wayside water, and at last the sight of it—magnificent front wheels supporting boiler-front and columnor chimney with its plume of smoke above, and the surprisingly sharp and full throated noise this made on broaching rising ground. And nearer there was sizzling and an added smell of hot oil, and hero worship for the two with blue jackets and smudged faces who controlled the marvellous thing, with its spinning flywheel and flashing rods.

Was not this creation a living work of art, and rightly revered? Surely then, nothing beyond a detail should ever be altered, certainly not its outline, merely for the sake of saving a little fuel or making it go faster: one cannot improve perfection.

Thus was the flywheel always on the left; the entrance always from a side; and wheel slats generally pointing upwards from the rear. There was latitude for the crossheads and forecarriage positions, although slipper bars and set-back fronts were deemed a little old-fashioned. Steering could be right or left and chimney tops should be copper, brass or cast, in makers' shape or have a plain iron ring. But always an engine should look like an engine, the large wheels and the flywheel emphasising its massiveness and the moving parts looking unbreakable and as if they would last for ever.

Wandering from established practice, as did Americans and Continentals, was frowned upon, and pictures showing rh flywheels, disk cranks, flimsy spokes, rear entrances and bulbous topped chimneys depicted a world of phantasy. (Nevertheless, most of the

143

makers, for a time, made straw burners, single speed colonial models with a flywheel clutch for belt tightening when going, and including many of the above objectionable features, which were shown in special catalogues.)

In England things stayed as they were, mostly, for the middle 40 years of the traction engine's life, as if there was a conspiracy between customer and manufacturer, the one to save appearances and the other costs. And the love is there still, welling up in these days of rallies with present-day owners, too, preferring their engines 'traditional'.

In these times one cannot expect it to be fully realised what 'Going with engines' meant. There was hard and dirty work, perhaps more than anything seen today and with an element of risk in it—as a factory inspector would think if he saw a driving belt flapping on a windy day and the unguarded small belts clicking round with fasteners proud above them. There were times when every bit of muscle and will was needed to do the pushing and pulling, chain-slinging, spud-cottar hammering and heaving up the last few sheaves on a rick bottom with the farm men left off because it's dinner time and you wanting to 'get finished and move'. This was in all weathers and sometimes midst choking dust. And now and then there would be ashpan and bars to remove, never without an eyefull of grit, to get at leaking stays, tubes or fusible plug. Then there were the natural enemies—policemen, road surveyors, bridge inspectors, private pond owners and if you lived in a van, the little things which sometimes shared it with you. Just some of the poetry was diluted then.

It was soon regained, however, after a spell on the belt at a new rick, with the governors going round and the steady rhythm casting its spell once more; as it did too on the fair-ground, and in the field when the rope-drum ratchet was tong-tong-tonging away while the other engine was pulling, and big-ends and balance weights were gently going over-and-over with glistening rods showing between them so as to get a little oil in ready for the next pull, and it was never far away either in day-dreams.